Calculator Decision-Making Sourcebook

A collection of facts, examples, information and techniques illustrating how you can use your *Advanced Professional Calculator* as a powerful decision-making tool — in business and everyday life situations.

Note: The calculator keystrokes and descriptions in this book were based on the TI-55 family of Advanced Professional Calculators, with *Algebraic Operating System*. The facts, information and examples included will be useful when working with *any* calculator, but the keystroke sequences described will only be similar when using an advanced calculator with AOS entry system.

This book was developed by:

The Staff of the Texas Instruments Learning Center

M. Dean LaMont
Lane L. Douglas
Dr. Ralph A. Oliva, Educational Software Director

And:

The Staff of the University of Denver Mathematics Laboratory

Dr. Ruth I. Hoffman, Director
Michael Zastrocky
James F. Reed
Dr. Sam Battaglia

With contributions by:

Harry Alderman
Dr. Paul Staiert
Dr. George Bardwell
Ross Wise
Joe Poyner

Artwork and layout were coordinated and executed by:

Deason and Schenck Associates

And:

Gaither and Davy Design Inc.

IMPORTANT

ISBN 0 − 89512 − 014 − 3

Library of Congress catalogue number: 77-18314

Table of Contents

Topic Reference Chart

$x \pm y$

To help you to use the techniques discussed in this book, the various cases we cover are tabulated here for you in this "you have/you need" table. Just locate the example or "case history" below which parallels the decision situation you're considering, and then refer to the specified section for a step-by-step analysis with keystrokes.

Information you have	Information you need or decision required	See pages
You have just acquired an "Advanced Professional Calculator" (such as *Texas Instruments TI-55*).	How to make use of all of its features & functions	**1**-1 to **1**-35*
Data on past performance	How to predict future performance using linear regression techniques	**2**-1 to **2**-6
Past data on advertising dollars versus sales volume	Predict effects of changing advertising expenditure	**2**-7 to **2**-10
Data for the past 5 years on stock dividends	Predict future performance— forecast dividend	**2**-11 to **2**-13
Data on 2 variables— employee aptitude test scores versus employee job performance	Determine if there *is* a relationship between these variables	**2**-14 to **2**-18
You've received a large shipment (called the "population") of spray cans; the manufacturer has made a claim on what their average weight will be.	Based on your *sample* data, you need to verify (to a degree of certainty you select) whether or not the *population* meets the manufacturer's claim.	**3**-3 to **3**-6
You're checking a large shipment of batteries with a claimed minimum lifetime.	You need to verify that the *population* meets the manufacturer's claim.	**3**-7 to **3**-9
You're checking a large batch of paint (population) to see if it meets requirements on dye content, based on data you have from a *small sample*.	You need to verify that specifications are met for the whole batch (population). Too much or too little dye will be grounds to reject the batch	**3**-10 to **3**-12
You need to verify that a shipment (population) of cough medicine does not exceed a specified alcohol content	You need to verify that the alcohol content of the *population* is *no greater* than specified.	**3**-13 to **3**-15

Information you have	Information you need or decision required	See pages
You're checking on a shipment (population) of parts to verify the manufacturer's claim that less than 12% of them are defective.	You need to verify the manufacturer's claim that 12% or less are defective. (Test on Proportions.)	3-16 to 3-18*
You have data on uncoated and coated pipe, and a manufacturer's claim that the coating process increases pipe lifetime to a certain level.	Based on a small number of test samples, you need to verify that the coating process creates a change in performance.	4-2 to 4-6
You have data on a group of experimental animals being tested for the effects of a certain drug	Based on a small number of test animals, you need to verify whether or not the drug creates any change.	4-7 to 4-11
The amount of a cash you *now have* in an account, and the interest rate.	Future value of the cash at various time intervals.	5-2 to 5-4*
A *future amount* you need to save for	How much you should deposit *now*	5-5
The amount of a regular series of payments you're making into an account	The future value of these payments at specified times.	5-6 to 5-8*
The amount of a series of payments you'll be receiving in the future, and the current bank interest rate	The present value of these payments (how much the payments are worth right now).	5-9 to 5-12
The amount of a loan you'll be making, the time period and interest rate for payback.	What should the *loan payments* to you be?	5-13 to 5-14
The current cost of a piece of equipment, the cost to "contract out" for the service performed by the equipment,	Should you buy the equipment and perform the service yourself, or contract to have it done?	5-15 to 5-17*
Cash amount you *have* available for an investment, rate of return you'd like, and a real estate investment opportunity	Should you invest? Can you achieve your desired rate of return?	5-18 to 5-20
Present cost of purchase — and of leasing — a large piece of equipment, as well as cash returns	a) Is it cheaper to lease or to buy the equipment? b) Is it a sound move to acquire the equipment at all?	5-21 to 5-23
How to use statistics and your calculator in making business decisions.	A brief look into the theory behind some of these techniques.	6-1 to 6-14

*Programming Examples

Introduction

Today, the way all of us deal with numbers and mathematics has been made easier by the hand-held calculator. A new speed, confidence, and accuracy are now possible in handling the "arithmetic" part of everyday life — for everyone! As hand-held calculators continue in their rapid evolution, higher power "advanced professional" machines — handling increasingly powerful mathematics — are becoming more and more available.

These machines bring a variety of powerful techniques right into the palm of your hand. Many techniques that previously required large volumes of tables, impossibly tedious calculations, or access to a large computer center can now be carried out in a few keystrokes on a hand-held machine.

This book focuses on how today's advanced professional calculators (like the *Texas Instruments TI-55*) can make it easier than ever before for you to use some of the powerful tools of statistics and the mathematics of finance in your everyday and business decision-making. We'll focus on situations taken from the world of business and finance, and get together basic facts which will allow you to use calculator methods in arriving at more accurate and secure conclusions. We'll be concentrating on the *"how to use"* side of these techniques, stating them in straightforward, step-by-step, layman's language — including examples with keystroke solutions along the way. For those of you who want a brief look at the details and theory, we'll include a brief survey of some of the basics of statistics, too. Most importantly, this book is directed at being sure you get the most out of your calculator — to be sure you're fully aware of what it will (and will not) do for you.

"Dear Pierre,..." or, The Story of Statistics

On some days it may seem that life itself (and business in particular) is just one big gamble. Appropriately enough the important science of statistics (as we now know it), traces its history to a gambler — a young nobleman from France. In 1654 Antoine Goubould, having the title of Chevalier de Méré, was

concerned over his luck at the gaming tables. He sought advice and counsel from the noted French mathematician, Blaise Pascal. Among the problems he put to Pascal was the question of how prize money should be divided among the players if a game is interrupted or "called off" for some reason.

This led Pascal into the study of probabilities — in particular he focused on the probability of one given player winning if a cancelled game were continued to completion. Pascal wrote a letter about these problems and his work on games of chance to another famous French mathematician, Pierre de Fermat. The resulting exchange of letters that followed was the beginning of the evolving science of statistics — whose methods are used in handling uncertain situations of all sorts today!

The Story of Calculators

Blaise Pascal was indeed an interesting and productive man — for while he was busy giving birth to the science of probability and statistics, he was also tinkering with what became one of the world's first "calculating machines" by building on the ideas of men such as John Napier. Pascal's work in this area began the evolution of the mechanical calculator — machines handling calculations rather slowly with the aid of complex entanglements of whirling gears, whizzing cranks, wheels, and windows. This evolution continued on up through 1890, when the punched card was pressed into data handling and calculating service-in helping to take the 1890 U.S. Census. This led the way to later electric relay devices which continued to evolve into large-scale computers.

Then, a few years ago, people working in the electronics industry made several breakthroughs that resulted in the *integrated circuit.* Integrated circuits made it possible to process and store large amounts of information, in very small spaces, with little power and at low cost. These devices, coupled with the development of the inexpensive *"Light Emitting Diode"* (LED) display made hand-held calculators a reality. Recent advances in integrated circuits (IC's) are continuing to increase the amount of information storage and processing that can be handled on a single IC "chip". (The term IC "chip" refers to the tiny piece of silicon upon which an integrated circuit is fabricated.)

New highly flexible "chips" are making today's "Advanced Professional" and Programmable hand-held machines possible. With these advanced machines anyone — almost anyplace — can with the touch of a key execute a highly complex mathematical calculation rapidly and accurately.

The "Calculator Decision-Making Sourcebook"

Mathematics — including the mathematics of statistics and finance — is all around us and is part of many activities in our everyday and business lives. Your calculator can help handle the mathematical side of life quickly and accurately — without having to hassle with lengthy computations. What's more, your advanced professional calculator can be a powerful ally as you handle decisions in your everyday and business life. This book has been designed to show you how.

What we've tried to do is put together a compact, accessible, step-by-step package of techniques enabling you to take a variety of decision-making situations and analyze them with keyboard solutions. This book was designed to work directly with your calculator, so be sure to use them together. Both of them have been designed for you.

An important first step is to get thoroughly acquainted with your calculator, to put it through its paces and to examine all aspects of its operation. *Chapter 1* of this book is a quick guided "tour" of all the features and keys of your calculator, along with brief examples illustrating the use of each feature. This "tour" is segmented into three major sections:

> 1) The keyboard basics
> 2) "Technical" functions and keys
> 3) Statistical functions and keys
> 4) Programming functions and keys

Touring in this fashion enables you to quickly get into the use of the *special powers* of your advanced machine — after briefly reviewing its basic operations.

The subsequent chapters in the book are packed with examples that illustrate how you can work with your machine in "Calculating Better Decisions". In each case a real life, business or financial situation is analyzed for you.

Each example is broken down into the following segments — each identified with its own graphic symbol, as shown:

Target: In each case the target is a brief statement of what types of calculation we'll be using to analyze the problem, and how to begin implementing the calculation.

Tools: The formulas and facts needed to "calculate the decision" along with a very brief statement as to *why* each is used, *where* the techniques come from, and *how* they are tailored to the specific example.

Keying It In: Sample keystrokes to execute the solution (using the data given in the example), along with what you'll see in the display at key points in the calculation.

Decision Time: How to use the results of your calculation in arriving at a conclusion or decision.

Going Further: For some examples, a "going further" section is also included — discussing how additional information or conclusions may be drawn from the calculation you've just completed.

While you're busy using your calculator, don't forget that even though it may be packed with the latest in solid state technology — it still qualifies as a great toy — for children of all ages. Play with it! Use it for exploring and "what iffing", as well as just idle doodling on the keys. You may just find yourself exploring patterns and relationships which can lead you to a new appreciation of the beautiful side of numbers and mathematics.

The Keys

A guided tour of the features
and functions of your Advanced
Professional Calculator.

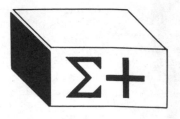

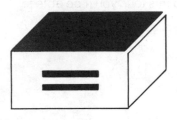

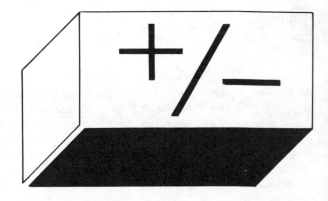

Introduction

The "Advanced Professional" hand calculator (of the *TI-55* family) is a genuine marvel, made possible by the most recent breakthroughs in semiconductor technology. A few short years ago we saw the advent of the *integrated circuit* — the device that made hand calculators possible. As the folks working in electronics have had time to "polish" their brainchild, they've found new ways to cram more and more information and problem solving ability onto a single silicon "chip". In addition, newer ways have been devised to make it *easy to use* the power on the chip.

Any calculator, however, is "no more functional than the knowledge of the person who operates it." As with any convenience or tool, whether it's a pen, wrench, car, radio or whatever, it's important to get the "feel" of it. Check out *all* of its features — get familiar with what it will (and will not) do for you. Many people never get to make use of all the power of their calculators — because they never take the few minutes necessary just to see each key in action!

To better help you get acquainted, this chapter is a quick, four-part "tour" of the essential features and keys of your calculator. We'll include some information on *why* each key is important, as well as *how* each works. After completing this tour, you'll be able to use *all* of the powers of your machine — for "around the house math" or in calculating better decisions.

The four sections of this "tour" are arranged as listed below. (If you're familiar with the basics of your calculator and need to know more right away about its advanced features — you may want to get right into *Section 2* or *3*).

Section 1 — The Keyboard Basics
    Basic mathematical features of your machine
Section 2 — "Technical" Functions and Keys
    Keys of special use in engineering and advanced math
Section 3 — Statistical Functions and Keys
    Special features and keys dedicated to speedy handling of statistical calculations.
Section 4 — Programming Functions and Keys
    A 32-step program memory allows you to key in a problem one time, then let the calculator rerun the problem…you just enter new variables.

Section 1: The Keyboard Basics

If you're looking at a new car, there are certain basic things that just have to be there—before you start adding on those extra "options". In this section we'll run through a quick tour of the "basics"—those features that allow you to handle the arithmetic part of mathematics quickly and accurately.

Please keep your calculator right with you as we go through the tour—check out each feature in turn. Turn it on! Here we go:

The DISPLAY

Whenever you first turn on your machine, you should see a single zero in the display indicating that all is well, the machine's on, and it's ready for action. Just *turning the calculator off and on clears everything inside to zero*. To check out your calculator's display, press the ⑧ key, the decimal point key ⊡ , the change sign key ⊞ , and then push the ⑧ key until the whole display is lit up. Check to be sure that all your decimal points light up as they move from right to left, and that all the parts of all of your 8's are lit up. You can enter up to 8 digits into your calculator at any one time. The leading 0 counts as one digit when entering decimal fractions. Notice that the negative sign stays immediately to the left of any negative number in the display, for easy reading.

That bright, friendly L.E.D. (Light Emitting Diode) display really has a powerful bundle of technology behind it. Each display segment is made up of little diodes made of Gallium Arsenide (GaAs), a substance which emits light when electric current is passed through it under just the right conditions.

Each number you see isn't lit up all at once, either. All the display segments are switched on and off very rapidly ("strobed") by the electronic "brain"—the silicon chip inside your calculator. The calculator does this trick so fast that your eye puts the segments together into numbers. Once the number is lit up, specially designed lens systems and colored windows are used to get the light to you as a clean, easy to read display.

Display Time Out

After typically 25-50 seconds of nonuse, the display goes blank except for a traveling decimal to conserve power. Press ⟨2nd⟩ twice to retrieve the display without affecting calculations.

To continue the tour press the clear key ⟨CLR⟩ in the upper right corner of keyboard, and read on.

2nd and INV : The "Dual Function" Keys

Your advanced professional calculator is crammed with functions to make everyday and business "decision" calculations easy and accurate. To allow you access to all of this power, without loading the machine with keys, many of the calculator keys have more than one function. The first function of the key is printed right on it. To use the first function on the key — just press it. The second function of a key is printed right above it. To use second functions, just press the 2nd key, and the key right below the function.

The inverse key INV , also provides additional calculator functions without increasing the number of keys on the keyboard. When you press the INV key before a particular function or key, the purpose of that function or key is *reversed*. The INV key works together with quite a few keys on your calculator to provide inverse functions, or to reverse an operation. In cases where you need to use *both* the 2nd and INV keys — you can use them in either order and get the same result; however, you must follow INV with 2nd in a program.

Clearing the Calculator

There are several procedures that allow you to clear various parts of your calculator, or to clear the entire machine — depending on your needs as you proceed through a problem.

■ CE — The CE (clear entry) key (lower left corner) clears the last number you entered into the calculator, as long as that number wasn't followed by a function or operation key. (So if you accidentally hit a 5 instead of a 6 in the middle of an entry, just hit CE and try again.) This key will also stop the display from flashing if you've created an error condition in your calculator. (An error condition exists when you ask your calculator to do something it can't do. It tries to do it anyway, finds out it can't, and flashes its display for help. See your owner's manual for details.) The CE key doesn't affect pending operations, what's stored in the memories, or calculated results.

■ CLR — The CLR (clear) key (upper right on your machine) essentially clears the entire machine, except for statistical data, what's stored in the memories and decimal settings made on the display format. (This key will also clear a flashing display.)

■ 2nd CA — Clear all key sequence — a clean sweep — clears out errors, memories (including program memory), registers, everything in the machine! You can also clear the entire machine by turning it OFF and ON, as mentioned earlier.

$\boxed{0}$ – $\boxed{9}$ $\boxed{\cdot}$ $\boxed{+/-}$ – Data Entry Keys

Your calculator operates with a full floating decimal point, and
numbers are entered into the machine with the data entry keys
$\boxed{0}$ – $\boxed{9}$ $\boxed{\cdot}$ $\boxed{+/-}$. As you enter any number, the decimal
point stays to the right of your entry until the decimal point key
is pressed. After pressing the decimal key ($\boxed{\cdot}$), the
fractional part of the number is keyed in, and the decimal point
floats to the left with it. To change the sign of a number in
the display, just push the change sign key $\boxed{+/-}$ once. (Pressing
$\boxed{+/-}$ again changes the sign back again.)

$\boxed{+}$ $\boxed{-}$ $\boxed{\times}$ $\boxed{\div}$ and $\boxed{=}$ – Basic Operation Keys

Basic arithmetic is handled with the 5 basic operation keys $\boxed{+}$
$\boxed{-}$ $\boxed{\times}$ $\boxed{\div}$ and $\boxed{=}$. Calculators like the *TI-55* have a
powerful feature called the *Algebraic Operating System* (AOS)
which makes problem solution with these keys exceptionally easy.
You just key in the problem the way it's written, press $\boxed{=}$, and get
your result. The amazing feature of AOS is that it automatically sorts
out *mixed operations* in a problem for you, and applies them in the
correct order as it calculates your result. (We'll say more about AOS
in the next section.)

When you press the $\boxed{=}$ key, all pending operations (things
waiting to happen inside your calculator) are completed. You get
your result, and the calculator is cleared — ready to start on the
next problem.

Example: Calculate
$15 + 7 \times 31 - 4 = ?$

Press   **Display/Comments**
15 $\boxed{+}$ 7 $\boxed{\times}$ 31 $\boxed{-}$ 4 $\boxed{=}$ **228.**

Note: *AOS* makes it easy to get the right answer in this example,
and not all calculators have it. You'll get different results for this
calculation on different machines. For more about AOS — see
next section.

AOS — The Algebraic Operating System

Mathematics is a science which adheres to a variety of rules. One such rule is that it never permits two different answers to the same series of operations. Because of this requirement — one solution for any computation — mathematicians have established a set of universally accepted rules when mixed operations are used in one calculation. For example, the problem:

$3 + 10 - 2 \times 14 \div 7 = ?$

has only one right answer! (Know what it is? It's 9.)

You can key this problem directly, left to right into your (*TI-55* type) calculator with AOS and you'll get the correct answer. The calculator sorts the operations you enter, applies them in the correct order, and lets you see what it's doing along the way. Your calculator (with AOS) performs operations it receives from you in the following universally accepted order:

1) Special Single Variable function keys — act on the displayed number immediately — as soon as you push the key. (We'll talk more about each of these keys later in the "tour" — but they include all the keys for the trig, log and hyperbolic functions and their inverses, as well as square and square root, factorial, percent, reciprocal and conversions.)
2) Percent change calculations are completed next.
3) Exponential calculations (y^x and $\sqrt[x]{y}$) are done next (we'll discuss these further in a following section.)
4) Multiplications and divisions are completed next, followed by
5) Additions and subtractions.

Finally, the equals key $\boxed{=}$ completes all operations.

When you were in elementary school you may have heard the memory aid (*My Dear Aunt Sally*) (MDAS) applied to help you remember the last part of this hierarchy (*multiplications and divisions* first, in order left to right — then *additions and subtractions* in the same way.) In a calculator equipped with AOS — all this is remembered for you.

There are cases in problem-solving where you may want to specify the order in which an expression is evaluated, or the way in which a problem is completed. In these cases *you* can control the order with the parentheses keys $\boxed{(}$ $\boxed{)}$, which are discussed in the next section. Parentheses demand a special first level of attention in mathematics — and they're treated that way by your calculator.

( ) – Parentheses Keys

In a variety of problems, *you* may need to specify the exact order in which expressions are evaluated, or the way in which numbers are grouped, as a problem is solved. Parentheses give you a way to "cluster" numbers and operations. By putting a series of numbers and operations in parentheses you tell the calculator: "Evaluate this little problem first – down to a single number result, then use this result for the rest of the calculation." *Within* each set of parentheses, your calculator will operate according to the rules of algebraic hierarchy. You should use the parentheses if you have any doubts in your mind about how the calculator will handle an expression.

Different calculators have different limits as to the number of parentheses that can be opened at one time, and how many "pending" operations can be handled. (The *TI-55* calculator allows you to open nine parentheses at one time, with up to four operations pending – exceeding these limits results in a flashing display.)

Note an important point when using parentheses. You may often see equations or expressions written with parentheses to indicate *implied multiplication:* $(2 + 1)(3 + 2) = 15$. *Your calculator will not perform implied multiplications.* You have to key in the operation between the parentheses:

$\boxed{(}$ 2 $\boxed{+}$ 1 $\boxed{)}$ $\boxed{\times}$ $\boxed{(}$ 3 $\boxed{+}$ 2 $\boxed{)}$ $\boxed{=}$ 15.

Here's an example on using parentheses:

Evaluate $\dfrac{(8 \times 4) + (9 \times -19)}{(3 + 10 \div 7) \times 2} =$

Solution: In problems of this type – you want the calculator to evaluate the entire numerator, then divide by the entire denominator. You can be sure of this taking place by placing an extra set of parentheses around the numerator and denominator as you key the problem in.

Press	**Display/Comments**
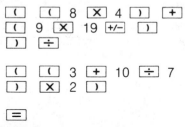	**32.** (8 x 4) displayed
	−139. The value of the numerator
	8.8571429 Value of denominator
	−15.693548 The final result.

| % | and | 2nd | Δ% | — Percent and Change Percent Keys

These keys are exceptionally handy ones — particularly for a wide variety of business and around the house percentage calculations.

| % | **Key** — When the | % | key is pressed, the number in the display is immediately converted to a decimal percent (multiplied by 0.01). If you enter 43.9 and press | % | , 0.439 is displayed.

The real power of the | % | key is turned on for you when you use it in combination with an operation key. This allows "mark up" and "mark down" as well as straight and inverted percentage problems to be solved. The rules for using the | % | key in these situations are tabulated below:

| + | n | % | = | adds n% to the original number displayed

| − | n | % | = | subtracts n% from the original number displayed

| × | n | % | = | multiplies the original number in the display by n%

| ÷ | n | % | = | divides the original number in the display by n%

| 2nd | Δ% | — The Change Percent (or "Delta Percent") Key Sequence

This very convenient key sequence calculates the *percentage change between two values*. This type of calculation comes up quite often in business and everyday situations. For example, let's say you keep pretty careful track of the mileage you get from your car and for a while it's been getting 17.0 miles per gallon (call this x_1). You get your car tuned up and the mileage jumps to 19.8 MPG (x_2).

What's the percent increase?
To do this on your calculator just:

Enter x_1, press | 2nd | Δ% | , enter x_2, press | = | , and the % change between x_1 and x_2 is calculated. (What your calculator displays is $\frac{x_1 - x_2}{x_2} \times 100$.)

Press

19.8 | 2nd | Δ% |

17

| = |

Display/Comments

19.8 Enter new mileage (x_1) and press | 2nd | Δ% |

17. Enter old mileage (x_2) and press | = |

16.470588 Percent change, about 16.5%.

MEMORY KEYS

There are 10 memories available for you to use in your calculator. These memories are special locations in the machine where you can store numbers you may need to use later on. The memories are a real bonus — and in many ways give you "11 calculators" in one, since you can store, recall or operate on the numbers in the memories without affecting calculations you have in progress in the "main machine".

The $\boxed{CE}$ and $\boxed{CLR}$ keys will not affect what's in the memories — but you can use the $\boxed{2nd}$ $\boxed{CA}$ key sequence to clear them all out if you need to. (Turning the calculator OFF and ON does this, too.)

Since you have 10 memories available you need to tell the machine *which one* you want to work with at any given time. As you'll see, every time you push a memory key you need to follow it immediately with the number of the memory you are using (n = 0 thru 9). This tells the machine which one of the 10 memories you're referring to at the moment. The operation of the memory keys is pretty much "common sense" as shown below:

IMPORTANT: Memories 1 through 7 are used internally when linear regression functions are used. Memories 8 and 9 are used internally when program locations 17 through 31 are used. When these situations exist, be sure to avoid using memories for number storage that may conflict with the internal operations.

$\boxed{STO}$ n — The Store Key

This key just "stores" the displayed number in the memory you specify with n. (n = 0 thru 9). (Any number previously stored in memory n is *cleared out first.*)

$\boxed{RCL}$ n — The Recall Key

Any time you press $\boxed{RCL}$ n, the number stored in memory n appears in the display and can be used in operations and calculations. The number remains in the memory after you press $\boxed{RCL}$ n, and you can recall any number from each of the ten memories as many times as you need to in any calculation. The number remains in a memory until you alter it with another memory key, the $\boxed{2nd}$ $\boxed{CA}$ clearing operation, or by turning the calculator off.

A quick example on the use of the memories:
$a = 10.3 (25 - 1.7)$
$b = 15a + 6$
$c = 20b$, and you need to find c.

Press

	Display/Comments
10.3 ⊠ ⊏ 25 ⊟ 1.7	Calculate and store a
⊐ ⊟	**239.99**
STO 0	**239.99** a stored in memory 0
15 ⊠ RCL 0 ⊞ 6 ⊟	**3605.85**
STO 1	**3605.85** b stored in memory 1
20 ⊠ RCL 1 ⊟	**72117.** The value of c.

Another way of looking at your memories is to consider that RCL n is a key sequence that can have any 10 (0 thru 9) values you decide. If you need some lengthy numerical value many times in a calculation — just store it in memory n. Every time you need the value later on — just hit RCL n and there it is!

There are a series of keys that let you *operate* on the numbers stored in memory without affecting other calculations in progress:

SUM n — **The Sum Key** — allows you to algebraically *add* whatever's in the display directly to what's stored in memory n (0 thru 9). (This doesn't affect any calculations in progress.) The result of the *addition* stays stored in the memory. *Note:* This process is *different* from what happens when you use the STO key. The STO n operation clears out what's in the memory, and replaces it with the number in the display.

INV SUM n — The *Subtract* key sequence, subtracts the number in the display from the number in memory n. The result stays stored in memory n (n = 0 thru 9).

2nd **Prod** n — The *"Multiply"* or *Product* key sequence, multiplies the number in memory n by what's in the display. The product stays stored in memory n (n = 0 thru 9).

INV **2nd** **Prod** n — The *"Divide"* or *Quotient* key sequence, divides the number in memory n by what's in the display. The quotient stays stored in memory n (n = 0 thru 9). (Note that the sequence **2nd** INV **Prod** n will perform the same memory division from the keyboard. However, the **2nd** must follow INV when used in a program.)

2nd **Exc** n — The *Exchange* key sequence just "swaps" what's in memory n with what's in the display. (The display value gets stored in memory n, while the number stored in memory n gets displayed.) This key is very handy in many problem situations — and allows you to make a quick "check" on what's in a memory without losing what's in the display. (Just press **2nd** **Exc** n twice.)

Section 2: "Technical" Functions and Keys

In this section we move on to discuss some of the features of your "Advanced Professional" calculator that are especially helpful in engineering, scientific, and some more advanced mathematical applications (applications that not too long ago used to be handled on mechanical sliderules). Many of these features have been made possible by some of the more recent developments in Integrated Circuit (IC) Technology — that allow calculator designers to "program" various functions and tables right into the IC chip. In this way you can put the calculator to work on a complex calculation with the touch of a key.

$\boxed{EE}$ — Scientific Notation Key

In many applications, particularly in science and engineering, you may find yourself needing to calculate with very large or small numbers. Such numbers are easily handled (by both you and your calculator) using *scientific notation*. A number in scientific notation is expressed as a base number (or "mantissa") times ten raised to some power (or "exponent").

$$\text{Mantissa} \times 10^{\text{power}}$$

To enter a number in scientific notation
- Enter the mantissa (then press $\boxed{+/-}$ if it's negative).
- Press $\boxed{EE}$ (Enter Exponent) — a "00" will appear at the right of the display.
- Enter the power of 10 (then press $\boxed{+/-}$ if it's negative).

A number such as $-3.8901448 \times 10^{-32}$ will look like this in your display:

In scientific notation the power of ten tells you where the decimal point would have to be if you were writing the number out in longhand. A positive exponent tells you how many places the decimal point should be shifted to the right, a negative exponent — how many places to the left. For example:

2.9979×10^8 equals $\quad 2.99790000.$

(Move decimal 8 places right, add zeroes as needed)

1.6021×10^{-19} equals $\quad .000\ 000\ 000\ 000\ 000\ 000\ 1.6021$

(Move decimal 19 places left, add zeroes as needed)

2nd Eng — Engineering Notation

Engineering notation is a modified form of scientific notation which is especially convenient in handling a variety of technical problems. Numbers displayed in engineering notation are expressed as a mantissa times 10 raised to a power, where the *mantissa and power are adjusted for convenient readout of units.* The mantissa has 1, 2 or 3 digits to the left of the decimal point; the power (or exponent) is always adjusted to a multiple of 3 (10^{12}, 10^{-6}, etc.). This allows the calculator to display results in units that are easily usable to the scientist or technician (such as 10^{-12} for picofarads, 10^{-3} for millimeters, 10^6 for megohms, etc.) 2nd ENG — can be pressed anytime — and the display enters into engineering notation. INV 2nd ENG — will remove this display mode, and so will 2nd CA .

2nd Fix n — Fix Decimal Control

This very convenient feature allows you to choose the number of digits you'd like to have displayed to the right of the decimal point as you go through your calculations:

Just press 2nd Fix , then press the desired number of decimal places (0 to 7).

The calculator will round all of your subsequent results to this number of decimal places. You can go on and make number entries with as many digits as you like, and the calculator will retain its own internal (11 digit) accuracy. The display value will continue to be correctly rounded to the number of decimal places you've selected. Note also that you can use the fix key to set the desired number of decimal places whether you're in standard display format, scientific notation, or engineering notation.

Example: $\frac{2}{3} = 0.6666667$

Press	Display/Comments
2nd CA	**0**
2 ÷ 3 =	**0.6666667**
2nd Fix 6	**0.666667** (*Note:* display
2nd Fix 2	**0.67** value is correctly
2nd Fix 1	**0.7** rounded)
2nd Fix 0	**1.**

The INV 2nd Fix , 2nd Fix 8 or 9, or 2nd CA key sequences can be used to return the display to standard format (2nd CA removes the number as well).

2nd π — "Pi" Key Sequence

The `2nd` `π` key sequence displays the first 8 digits of π. (Eleven digits are entered into the calculator — 8 correctly rounded digits are displayed.) The number you'll see displayed is: 3.1415927. This key sequence displays π immediately, doesn't affect calculations in progress, and can be used anytime in a calculation.

2nd x! — "Factorial" Key Sequence

The `2nd` `x!` key sequence calculates and displays the factorial of the number in the display. The factorial of any number x is written $x!$, and is equivalent to $(1 \times 2 \times 3 \times 4 \times ... \times x)$. (0! is 1 by definition). Your calculator will calculate the factorial for any integer less than 70. (Non integer entries cause a flashing display when `2nd` `x!` is pressed — entries over 69 cause the calculator to "overflow" when `2nd` `x!` is pressed.)

The `2nd` `x!` sequence can be used at any time in a calculation. It acts immediately on the number in display, and doesn't affect calculations in progress. $x!$ is used in a variety of problems involving the laws of probability.

x² √x 1/x — Square, Square Root and Reciprocal Keys

These 3 easily accessible keys are essentials for speedily handling a variety of algebraic and equation solving situations. All three of these keys act immediately on the number in the display (x), and don't affect calculations in progress.

`x²` — *The Square Key* — calculates the square of the number in the display (multiplies the displayed number by itself).

`√x` — *Square Root Key* — Calculates the square root of the number in the display. The square root of a number (say x) is another number (labeled $\sqrt{x}$) such that $(\sqrt{x}) \times (\sqrt{x}) = x$

`1/x` — *Reciprocal Key* — Divides the displayed number *into* one.

Here's an example to put them all together: $\dfrac{(\sqrt{\pi + 4!})}{\left(\dfrac{1}{15}\right)^2} = ?$

Press

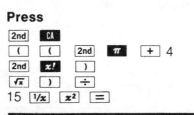

| 2nd | CA |
| ((2nd π + 4 |
| 2nd x!) |
| √x) ÷ |
| 15 1/x x² = |

Display/Comments

0 Clear all

27.141593 This is $\pi + 4!$
5.2097594 This is $\sqrt{\pi + 4!}$
1172.1959 The final result.

y^x — Universal Power Key

This powerful key allows you to raise any (positive) number to any
power at the touch of a key. To use this key:
- Enter the number you want to raise to a power (y)
- Press y^x
- Enter the power (x)
- Press $=$ (or any operation key)

Example: Calculate $3.1897^{4.7343}$

Press	Display/Comments
[2nd] CA	**0** Clear machine
3.1897 y^x	**3.1897** "y" value
4.7343	**4.7343** "x" value
$=$	**242.60674** Final result: y^x

The universal power key is an extremely useful one that we'll be
using quite a bit in "Calculating Better Decisions" — particularly
in problems involving cash flows and the present value of money.

$x\sqrt{y}$ — Universal Root Key

This key allows you to take any root of any positive number, without
a lot of hassle. (Before calculators came along, calculations like
this were usually pretty time consuming — and involved a set of
logarithm tables.) To use this key:
- Enter the number you want to take the root of (y)
- Press $x\sqrt{y}$
- Enter the root you want to take (x)
- Press $=$ (or another operation key)

Example: Calculate $\sqrt[3.871]{21.496}$

Press	Display/Comments
[2nd] CA	0
21.496 $x\sqrt{y}$	**21.496** "y" value
3.871	**3.871** "x" value
$=$	**2.2089685** Final result.

$x{:}y$: You may, in some calculating situations, want to reverse the
roles of x and y in y^x and $x\sqrt{y}$ calculations, after they've been
entered. The "x swap y" key does just that for you — if you need to
do it.

2nd Const — Calculations with a Constant

Here is a genuine labor saving (and accuracy increasing) feature of your calculator! The 2nd Const key sequence stores *a number and an operation* for use in repetitive calculations. Once the number and operation are stored, you just key in the numbers you want them to work on, press ═ , and you get your answer. Calculations using the 2nd Const feature can be repeated as many times as you need them! Here's how it works:

■ Enter the operation you want to work with it
■ Enter the repetitive number m
■ Press 2nd Const

From then on in, you just:

■ Enter the number you want to operate on
■ Press equals ═

The 2nd Const feature works in the following way with certain operation keys on your machine:

+	m	2nd	Const	adds m to each subsequent entry
−	m	2nd	Const	subtracts m from each subsequent entry
×	m	2nd	Const	multiplies each subsequent entry by m
÷	m	2nd	Const	divides each subsequent entry by m
y^x	m	2nd	Const	raises each subsequent entry to the mth power — it calculates y^m
$^x\sqrt{y}$	m	2nd	Const	takes the mth root of each subsequent entry — calculates $\sqrt[m]{y}$
2nd	Δ%	m 2nd	Const	Calculates the percentage change between each subsequent entry x_1 and m.

It computes $\dfrac{x_1 - m}{m} \times 100$.

Example: Multiply 2, 4, 6 and 8 by π.

Press	Display/Comments
2nd CA	**0**
2 × 2nd π 2nd Const	**3.1415927** π
═	**6.2831853** 2π
4 ═	**12.566371** 4π
6 ═	**18.849556** 6π
8 ═	**25.132741** 8π

Note: Pressing CLR or 2nd CA (as well as operation and function keys) removes the automatic constant.

$\boxed{\ln x}$, $\boxed{2nd}$ $\boxed{\log}$ — Logarithms

Logarithms are mathematical functions that enter into a variety of technical and theoretical calculations. In addition, they form an important part of many mathematical "models" of natural phenomena. The logarithm keys give you immediate access to the "log" of any number—without having to hassle with bulky tables.

$\boxed{\ln x}$ —*The Natural Logarithm Key*—immediately displays the *natural logarithm* (base e − 2.7182818) of the number in the display. (*Note:* the number in the display should be positive—attempting to take $\boxed{\ln x}$ of a negative number will result in a flashing display.)

$\boxed{2nd}$ $\boxed{\log}$ —*The Common Logarithm Key*—immediately displays the common logarithm (base 10) of the value in the display (display should be positive).

$\boxed{e^x}$, $\boxed{2nd}$ $\boxed{10^x}$ —e^x *and Powers of 10 Keys*—e^x and 10^x are the "inverse" or "anti" functions of logarithms. ($e^{(\ln x)} = x$, and $10^{(\log x)} = x$.) These calculations arise in many technical situations and can be handled in a keystroke on your calculator.

$\boxed{e^x}$ —*e to the Power x Key*—Raises e to the power of the number in the display (calculates the natural antilogarithm of the number in the display).

$\boxed{2nd}$ $\boxed{10^x}$ —*10 to the Power x Key*—Raises 10 to the power of the number in the display (calculates the common antilogarithm of the display value).

Notes on logarithm and "anti" logarithm keys:
■ Each of these keys acts immediately on the number in the display—and doesn't affect calculations in progress.
■ Different calculators use a variety of "routines" for arriving at these values. Certain limits are set by these routines—and exceeding them may result in an error indication—see your owner's manual for details.

Some examples: Calculate log 15.32, ln 203.451, $e^{-.69315}$, 10^π

Press	**Display/Comments**
15.32 $\boxed{2nd}$ $\boxed{\log}$	**1.1852588**
203.451 $\boxed{\ln x}$	**5.3154252**
.69315 $\boxed{+/-}$ $\boxed{e^x}$	**0.4999986**
$\boxed{2nd}$ $\boxed{\pi}$ $\boxed{2nd}$ $\boxed{10^x}$	**1385.4557**

2nd Deg , 2nd Rad , 2nd Grad — Angular Mode Keys

Your calculator is equipped to handle a variety of calculations that involve angles — notably the trigonometric functions and polar/rectangular conversions. When performing these calculations, your calculator allows you to select any one of three common units for angular measure using the key sequences below:

2nd Deg — selects degree mode. In this mode all entered or calculated angles are measured in degrees, until another mode is selected.

(one degree equals $\frac{1}{360}$ of a circle — a right angle equals 90°)

2nd Rad — selects radian mode. In this mode all angles are measured in radians (one radian equals $\frac{1}{2\pi}$ of a circle — a right angle equals $\frac{\pi}{2}$ radians).

2nd Grad — selects grad mode. In this mode all angles are measured in grads (one grad equals $\frac{1}{400}$ of a circle — a right angle equals 100 grads).

Note that when you first turn your calculator on — *it powers up in the degrees mode* and stays in that mode until a new mode is selected.

sin cos tan — Trigonometric Keys

Immediately calculate the sine, cosine and tangent of the angle in the display (angle is measured in units of selected angle mode).

The trig functions relate the angles and sides of a right triangle as shown below:

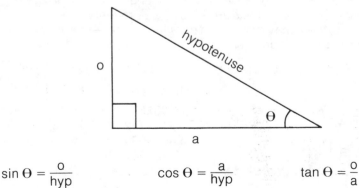

$$\sin \Theta = \frac{o}{hyp} \qquad \cos \Theta = \frac{a}{hyp} \qquad \tan \Theta = \frac{o}{a}$$

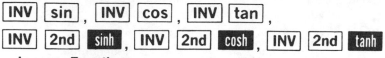
2nd sinh , 2nd cosh , 2nd tanh

— The Hyperbolic Function Keys

Immediately calculate the hyperbolic sine, hyperbolic cosine, or hyperbolic tangent of the number in the display. These functions operate in similar fashion to the "trig" functions — and are used in a variety of advanced engineering and mathematical applications.

INV sin , INV cos , INV tan ,
INV 2nd sinh , INV 2nd cosh , INV 2nd tanh

Inverse Functions

Using the INV preceding another key reverses the operation and intention of that key. When used with the trig or hyperbolic functions — the inverses of these functions are obtained.

INV sin , INV cos , and INV tan — In these key sequences, an angle is calculated (in the units of the mode selected) whose sine, cosine or tangent is in the display. (These key sequences calculate the arcsine ($\sin^{-1}$), arccosine ($\cos^{-1}$), and arctangent ($\tan^{-1}$), respectively.)

Likewise the:

INV 2nd sinh , INV 2nd cosh , and INV 2nd tanh — key sequences calculate the hyperbolic arcsine ($\sinh^{-1}$), hyperbolic arccosine ($\cosh^{-1}$) and hyperbolic arctangent ($\tanh^{-1}$), respectively.

For limits and special features of these functions — refer to your owner's manual.

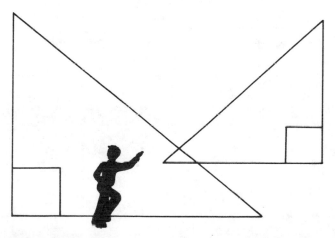

Conversions

A powerful convenience made possible by new high density,
integrated circuit technology, is the availability of conversions on
your calculator. Seven basic conversions are available on
calculators of the *TI-55* family — and they're simple to use, so
take advantage of them. The conversion keys are each labeled with
two units in "from-to" order. To perform the basic conversions, just
enter the value you want to convert, and follow the key sequences
as shown below:

Key Sequence	Converts Number entered	To	Final number Displayed
2nd DMS·DD	Degrees, minutes, seconds (DDD. mm ss)	→	Decimal Degrees (DDD . dd)
2nd °F·°C	Fahrenheit (°F)	→	Celsius (Centigrade) (°C)
2nd D·R	Degrees	→	Radians
2nd G·R	Grads	→	Radians
2nd in·mm	Inches	→	Millimeters
2nd gal·l	Gallons (U.S.)	→	Liters
2nd lb·kg	Pounds (av)	→	Kilograms

*Note: To perform any conversions in the "reverse direction"
(opposite to the arrow), just hit the* INV *key right before the
conversion sequence.*

2nd P→R — Polar to Rectangular Conversions

This is an especially handy feature of your calculator that is
particularly useful in science and engineering applications.
Working with the x:y key — it's fast and easy to convert from polar
to rectangular coordinates, or vice versa. Just follow the key
sequences illustrated below:

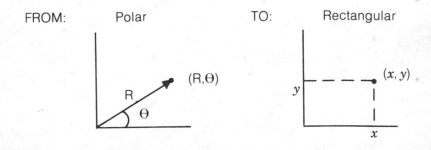

please

ENTS

RUMENTS CALCULATOR
OLITAN AREAS

is
chusetts
s
ia
gan
nnsylvania

(ter date)

Phoenix, Arizona
Washington, D.C.
Canada only
Calgary, Alberta
Toronto, Ontario
Montreal, Quebec
Vancouver, B. C.

Texa
831 !
El Se
Telef

Texa
140 !
San l
Telef

Texa
776 l
Sunn
Telef

Texa
#1 H
Melvi
(Exit
Telef

Texa:
9725
Suite
Denv
Telef

Texa:
2420
(Near
Telex

g the unit to the TI Service Facility for repair
culator of the same model by bringing the
listed below. Out-of-warranty calculators will
not exceed 50 percent of the latest suggested
for six months. For additional information,

TEXAS INSTRUMENTS
INCORPORATED

ANNOUNCING A NEW SERVICE FOR TEXAS INST
OWNERS IN THE FOLLOWING METROP

San Francisco (and Bay Area), California

Los Angeles, California

Portland, Oregon

Dallas, Texas

Denver, Colorado

New York (and New Jersey)

Ft. Lauderdale, Florida

Tulsa, Oklahoma

Chicago, Illino

Boston, Massa

Houston, Tex

Atlanta, Georg

Detroit, Michi

Pittsburgh, Pe

(Other offices will be opened at la

If your Texas Instruments calculator requires service, instead of sendin
you may elect to exchange the calculator for a factory rebuilt ca
calculator in person to the nearest Texas Instruments exchange office
be exchanged for a flat fee based on the latest repair rates, which will
retail price of the calculator, and the exchange unit will be in warrant

To convert *from* polar *to* rectangular coordinates:
- ■ Enter your value for "R"
- ■ Press [x:y]
- ■ Enter your "Θ" value (units selected with mode key)
- ■ Press [2nd] [P→R]

"y" is now displayed, to read "x":
- ■ Press [x:y]

"x" is now displayed.

FROM: Rectangular   TO: Polar

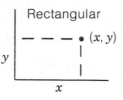
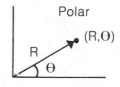

To convert *from* rectangular *to* polar coordinates:
- ■ Enter your "x" value
- ■ Press [x:y]
- ■ Enter your "y" value
- ■ Press [INV] [2nd] [P→R]

"Θ" is now displayed (in units selected by mode key), to read "R":
- ■ Press [x:y]

"R" is now displayed.

Example:

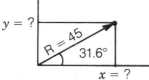

Convert R = 45 meters, Θ = 31.6°
into rectangular coordinates

Press	**Display/Comments**
Turn calculator OFF and ON	**0** Calculator is in degree mode
45 [x:y] 31.6	Enter polar coordinates
[2nd] [P→R]	**23.579366** "y" value
[x:y]	**38.327712** "x" value

Section 3: Statistical Functions and Keys

In this section of our "tour" we'll be examining some of the "high power options" on your calculator—the ones that give it real punch in helping you in calculating better decisions. These keys and features are really keeping track of quite a bit of complex mathematics for you—so that you can focus your attention on using and analyzing the results.

Knowledge of the detailed statistical theory behind the use and functions of these keys and features would take quite a while to cover and is beyond the scope of this book. In this section we'll clearly outline these functions with step-by-step procedures for using each of them. Later chapters in this book are crammed with examples illustrating how to use these keys as part of decision making in your everyday and business life. As you'll see—it's not necessary to have a detailed background in statistics to use the tools it provides. With your advanced professional calculator as an ally—it's a cinch. (For those of you who want a brief review of some theory—see *Chapter 6*.)

Mean and Standard Deviation

In many situations in your business (and everyday life), you may find yourself handling a large set of *data points*. (This data could be test scores, sales figures, weights of an incoming shipment, etc.) The most commonly used statistical calculations used to "boil down" that data are the *mean,* and *standard deviation.* The *mean* (or *average* value) is the most common "central" tendency in your data. The *standard deviation* gives you a feel for how variable the data is—a feel for how far the data differs from the mean.

Your calculator has special features allowing you to speedily *enter* data, and calculate the mean and standard deviation. Here's the step-by-step procedure:
■ Begin any statistical calculations with [2nd] [CA]
■ Enter each Data Point, then press the [Σ+] key (If you make an incorrect data entry, you can remove it by rekeying the error, and pressing [2nd] [Σ-] .)
Note: As you enter your data with the [Σ+] key, your calculator keeps track of the number of points you enter in the display.

When all your data is entered:
■ Press [2nd] [Mean] — to calculate the mean value for the data.

■ Press [2nd] [S.Dev.] — to calculate the Standard Deviation for sample data.
■ Press [2nd] [Var] [√x] — to calculate the *Standard Deviation* for population data.

Note: The difference between the Sample Standard Deviation and the Population Standard Deviation calculations becomes very small for over 30 data points. A *population* is usually a large set of items, and a *sample* is a smaller portion selected from the population. We'll be talking more about these terms in later chapters of the book.

Example: You're teaching a course, and the first set of test scores is in. You'd like to see how well the class is doing. The scores are tabulated below:

96	65	81
85	76	86
57	98	75
78	100	72
81	70	80

Press	**Display/Comments**
[2nd] [CA]	**0** Be sure to clear the entire machine
96 [Σ+]	**1.** The calculator counts
85 [Σ+]	**2.** your data points for you
Continue for all points	
72 [Σ+]	**14.**
80 [Σ+]	**15.**
[2nd] [Mean]	**80** Class average
[2nd] [Var] [√x]	**11.564313** "Spread"

Note: Using these statistical functions "ties up" 7 memories of your calculator — and you may run into trouble if there's data in them before you start:

memory 1 contains — intermediate calculations.
memory 2 contains — the sum of all your x-data points.
memory 3 contains — the sum of the squares of all x-points.
memory 4 contains — the sum of x times y.
memory 5 contains — the sum of all your y-data points.
memory 6 contains — the sum of the squares of all y-points.
memory 7 contains — the number of data points.

Linear Regression — "Telling the Future"

"Linear Regression" may sound like a highly technical or threatening title to you — but it's a process that your calculator makes very easy to use. And — it's one that deals with one of the oldest problems in the world for the businessman — predicting the future. With the linear regression keys on your calculator you can take data about past performance or relationships and use it to make forecasts of future performance (assuming that whatever relationship is at work keeps on working). *Chapter 2* goes into detail on how to use linear regression and what it's all about, so we'll just briefly discuss here the keys you'll be using.

In the linear regression situation, you usually have data expressed as pairs of variables that you could plot on a graph. We usually label a pair of points like this with the letters (x,y) (x may be dollars in advertising while y is unit sales or x may be a test score and y a performance record in the field, etc.). You want to make a prediction: For any given *x value that you select* — what will happen to y (or vice versa)? Your calculator can do this for you by mathematically drawing the "best straight line" through your data points. You may then use the straight line to make predictions. Here are the simple steps you follow to do this:

■ First, press 2nd   CA — do this when starting any statistical calculation.
■ Enter an "x" value and press x:y
    — then —
■ Enter the corresponding "y" value, and press Σ+
■ Continue until all data points are entered.

Your calculator is now ready to draw the best straight line through your points, and give you the following information from it:

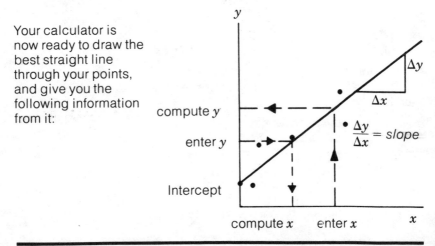

■ Press `2nd` `Slope` to calculate the slope of the calculator's line through your points.
■ Press `2nd` `Intcp` to calculate the y-intercept of the calculator's line.

To estimate a y value for any given x value you select:
■ Enter x and press `2nd` `y'` — the corresponding y value is displayed.

To estimate an x value for any y value you select:
■ Enter y and press `2nd` `x'` — the corresponding x value is displayed.

To get a feel for how well the two sets of variables are related:

■ Press `2nd` `Corr` — the calculator displays the *correlation coefficient* of the data. A value close to one indicates a "good" relationship between the sets of data, a value near zero indicates that there's little relationship between your x and y values.

Note: If, as you're entering your data, you need to *remove* any data points use the following key sequence:
■ Re-enter the undesired x value
■ Press `x:y`
■ Re-enter the undesired y value
■ Press `2nd` `Σ-`

After your data is entered, you can get some further information:
`2nd` `Mean` , `2nd` `S.Dev.` , `2nd` `Var` calculates the mean, standard deviation and variance of your y data points.
`INV` `2nd` `Mean` , `INV` `2nd` `S.Dev.` , `INV` `2nd` `Var` calculates the mean, standard deviation and variance of your x data points.

Standard deviation is computed with N-1 weighting and variance is computed with N weighting.

Trend Line Analysis

Trend line analysis is a variation of linear regression that's very
handy in making predictions based on trends or growth. There are
extra special features in your advanced professional calculator that
provide for easy and rapid trend line analysis predictions. A
complete discussion of these features and how to use them in
business decision situations is included for you in *Chapter* 2.
We'll go through a brief "tour" of the process here.

The only thing that makes trend line analysis different from linear
regression is that the x values are *automatically* increased by 1 for
each data point. Your calculator does this for you all by itself—all
you need to do is enter the first x value with the $\boxed{x{:}y}$ key, and then
enter *consecutive* y values with the $\boxed{\Sigma+}$ key. Your machine will
automatically increment the x variable by one for each y value
you enter.

Once all your data is entered, you've got all of the information, at
your fingertips, that was available in the linear regression
calculation. Your calculator draws the "best fitting line" through the
data. You can use the calculator to:

    Predict a y value for any x you select. Enter x, press $\boxed{\text{2nd}}$ $\boxed{y'}$
    Predict an x value for any y you select. Enter y, press $\boxed{\text{2nd}}$ $\boxed{x'}$
    Calculate the slope of the line: Press $\boxed{\text{2nd}}$ $\boxed{\text{Slope}}$
    Calculate the intercept of the line: Press $\boxed{\text{2nd}}$ $\boxed{\text{Intcp}}$
    See how well the data points are related. Press $\boxed{\text{2nd}}$ $\boxed{\text{Corr}}$

Note: If you make an error while you're keying in your data, you can
use the following sequence to remove the bad point:

    Bad point in display
    Press $\boxed{\Sigma+}$
        —then—
    Press $\boxed{x{:}y}$, −1 $\boxed{=}$ $\boxed{x{:}y}$
    Re-enter the bad point
    Press $\boxed{\text{2nd}}$ $\boxed{\Sigma-}$
    Enter the correct point
    Press $\boxed{\Sigma+}$
    Continue

Example: A company started business in 1972, and you've been watching its growth fairly closely. Its profits for successive years have been:

Year	Profits (millions of dollars)
1972	−1.2
1973	−0.3
1974	2.1
1975	1.8
1976	2.7

What will you predict the profit level to be in 1978 and 1980?
For what year will you predict profits of $10 million?

Press	**Display/Comments**
2nd -CA-	**0** Clear all
2nd Fix 2	**0.00** Set decimal to 2 places
1972 x:y 1.2 +/− Σ+	**1.00** Enter first x and y value
0.3 +/− Σ+	**2.00** Calculator automatically
2.1 Σ+	**3.00** increases x value by one
1.8 Σ+	**4.00** for each subsequent
2.7 Σ+	**5.00** y value

To predict sales in 1977 and 1980

| 1977 2nd y′ | **3.99** |
| 1980 2nd y′ | **6.96** |

To predict when sales will reach $10,000,000

| 10 2nd x′ | **1983.07** |

To check on the correlation between these two sets of data:

| 2nd Corr | **0.93** a good correlation |

Section 4: Programming Functions and Keys

Your calculator is a powerful problem-solving device, equipped with a variety of features that are ready to use—right from the keyboard. In addition, though, your calculator is programmable. This means you can teach your calculator to "push its own buttons" to automatically perform a variety of calculations. You can teach your calculator up to 32 problem-solving steps, and then have it execute these steps as often as you like—with a simple key sequence. In this chapter we'll go on a tour of the keys on your machine especially devoted to programs and programming.

What's Happening Inside

The way your calculator "learns" a program is in reality quite simple. There's a special memory, called a "program memory" inside your machine, that remembers the program keystrokes you teach it. As you program your machine, each keystroke sequence you enter is stored in order in this memory as a simple code. When you've finished entering a program, your calculator can then go back, read the "codes" in order, and push its own buttons for you in the exact sequence you've taught it.

To enter a program, you use the programming keys clustered as second functions across the bottom row of your keyboard. These keys let you teach the calculator the necessary problem-solving keystrokes. When you've taught your calculator a program, it's as if you've set up "tracks" for it to run on—a path for it to follow in solving your problem. When the calculator is programmed and ready to go, you can start it off at the beginning of these tracks and, much like a train, run down the line of steps you've entered. The "track" is your program—stored in program memory—and the "train" is your calculator running the program. As the train on the program track comes to (or points to) each step you've programmed, the calculator pushes its own buttons for you as it was directed.

A SIMPLE PROGRAMMING EXAMPLE

Let's take a look at a quick example to show you how programming can help you save time and improve your calculation accuracy. Consider this situation. You've just received a special sale notice from a department store indicating that all the items listed in their current sale catalog will be marked down an additional 15% for one day only. There are several items that you are interested in, so you pull out your calculator and start working:

Price ⎡−⎤ 15 ⎡%⎤ ⎡=⎤ . If you want to check the sale price of 25 different items, you'll have to work this key sequence 25 different times. However, calculations like this that have to be done over and over are a cinch for your programmable calculator. All you have to do is enter the program to solve this once into your calculator — and then all you'll need to do is enter the price of the item, start the program with one key sequence, and the calculator will automatically push all the keys in the program for you. Let's see how this works.

First you press the [2nd] [Lrn] sequence to "turn on" the program memory of your calculator. When you do this, the display changes to a unique format to tell you it's ready to learn and remember the keystrokes you tell it.

00 00

The left two digits are used to show the program step number (from 00 to 31) and the right two are used for the key number codes (more on this in a minute).

After turning on the program memory, just key in the keystrokes needed to solve the problem. Then you turn off the program memory by pressing [2nd] [Lrn] again and you're ready.

Now, let's program the Price ⎡−⎤ 15 ⎡%⎤ ⎡=⎤ problem.

Press	**Display/Comments**
[2nd] [CA] [2nd] [Lrn]	**00 00** Clears calculator completely and gets into learn mode.
⎡−⎤ 15 ⎡%⎤ ⎡=⎤	**05 00** This sequence takes the display value (entered separately for each problem) and subtracts the 15% discount from it.

(Notice that the step counter has advanced to 05 showing that you've used steps 00 through 04 for your program.)

At this point you need to do one more thing.

Now that the calculator has the answer, you need to tell it to stop and show the result. This is accomplished with the [2nd] [R/S] sequence.

Press
[2nd] [R/S]

Display/Comments
06 00 Tells the program to stop and display the result.

The [2nd] [R/S] sequence is the Run/Stop sequence. When it's used inside a program it tells the calculator to stop and display the result. [2nd] [R/S] is also used to "run" or start a program when you're ready for it to run.

Now since you've finished the program, you need to leave the "learn mode". Pressing [2nd] [Lrn] again does this for you.

Press
[2nd] [Lrn]

Display/Comments
0

Now you're almost ready to run. One more key sequence must be used—the [2nd] [Rst] sequence. This is the *reset* operation that puts the program back to step 00, the start of the program. Each time you run the program you must start at the beginning, step 00. [2nd] [Rst] gets you there.

Let's find the reduced prices on these items discounted 15%: $9.95, $12.95, and $49.95. Since we're working with money, let's fix the decimal at two places.

Press

[2nd] [Fix] 2

[2nd] [Rst]
9.95 [2nd] [R/S]
12.95 [2nd] [Rst]

[2nd] [R/S]
49.95 [2nd] [Rst]
[2nd] [R/S]

Display/Comments

0.00 Fix decimal at two places.
0.00 Reset to step 00.
8.46 9.95 − 15% = $8.46
12.95 Enter new price and reset to 00.
11.01 New discount price
49.95 Enter price and reset.
42.46 Discount price

You can work this problem over and over just by entering the price to be discounted, resetting the program, and starting it.

Using 2nd Rst as a Program Step

As you can see from the above example, programming can save you many steps when you do repetitive type calculations. We can, however, improve the "discount" program by including reset (2nd Rst) as part of the program. That way you don't have to reset each time. Let's do this now.

Press	**Display/Comments**
2nd CA 2nd Lrn	**00 00** Clears calculator and gets into learn mode.
─ 15 % = 2nd R/S	**06 00** Calculates discount price.
2nd Rst	**07 00** This adds an "automatic reset" into the program. Each time you work a problem the program comes to the 2nd R/S and stops. Then when you enter a new price and push 2nd R/S , the program starts at step 07, sees the reset, goes back to step 00 and calculates the discount price and stops.
2nd Lrn 2nd Rst	**0** Comes out of learn mode and resets for first calculation.

To check out the program, let's find the discount price for these items: $14.95, $7.50, and $24.75.

Press	**Display/Comments**
2nd Fix 2	**0.00** Fix decimal at two places
14.95 2nd R/S	**12.71**
7.5 2nd R/S	**6.38**
24.75 2nd R/S	**21.04**

These examples have shown you the basic operation of the programming keys on your calculator, however, let's take a more detailed look at them now.

PROGRAMMING KEYS

As we've mentioned, your calculator has a 32-step program memory, steps 00 through 31. Each step in program memory can hold one key function or keystroke. The 2nd key alone does not use a program step, but is used to identify the second-function key that does count as a step. CAUTION: The storage space for program steps 17 through 25 and 26 through 31 is shared with memories 9 and 8 respectively. For example, if the program goes past step 16 (through step 25) memory 9 cannot be used; if steps 26 through 31 are used, memory 8 cannot be used.

2nd Lrn — The Learn Key

A program is entered into the program memory by pressing 2nd Lrn for the "learn mode", pressing the keys to solve a problem, and then pressing 2nd Lrn again to exit the "learn mode".

You can tell then the calculator is in the "learn mode" by a special four-digit display.

00 00

The left two digits indicate the program step number (00 through 31). (Note that the calculator will automatically exit the learn mode when the 32nd key function is entered). The right two digits in the learn-mode display show zeros when first entering a program because the calculator advanced to the next program step as you enter the program. However, once a program is entered, you can go back and check or change your program because a two-digit number or key code is displayed in the right two digits.

Refer to Using Key Codes for more information on these.

2nd R/S — The Run/Stop Key

As the name Run/Stop implies, the 2nd R/S key has two functions. If a program is not running, this key is used to run or start the program. Likewise, if a program is running, this key will stop the program. When used as a program step 2nd R/S is the way to tell the calculator to stop and display an answer or wait for a new entry. When 2nd R/S is manually pressed to stop a running program, the exact program step cannot be predetermined. A program should contain at least one 2nd R/S instruction except when 2nd Rst is used to produce a continuous loop program. Otherwise, the calculator will flash a zero.

2nd   Rst   — The Reset Key

The function of the Reset Key is to reset the program step number
back to 00 (the beginning of the program). When used manually,
the reset to 00 takes place with no other action. When 2nd   Rst   is
encountered as a program step, the program operation immediately
returns to step 00 and automatically continues running. Using
2nd   Rst   in a program without 2nd   R/S   is called a loop
program. A loop program can be stopped by pressing 2nd   R/S
An error condition (flashing display) will also stop the program.

2nd   Sst   — The Single-Step Key

Pressing 2nd   Sst   causes the program step number to advance
to the next step. When in the learn mode, pressing 2nd   Sst   allows
you to single step through the program and check the key codes
as they are displayed for each step. When not in the learn mode, the
key function of the program step is performed as if pressed on the
keyboard. This single-step operation allows you to observe the
display while each program step is performed one step at a time.
IMPORTANT: When 2nd   R/S   is encountered as a program step
while using the single-step key (not in learn mode), the program will
begin running from that point and will result in a flashing display if
another 2nd   R/S   or 2nd   Rst   is not in the program.

Using Key Codes

When in the learn mode, the right-hand two digits in the display indicate the key code of the operation to be performed at that program step.

The key code your calculator uses to indicate each step is a fairly straightforward one. The two digits simply represent the row and column respectively of the key in question (except for the number keys ⌷0⌷ through ⌷9⌷ which are represented by their number; 05 represents ⌷5⌷ , etc.). For second functions on your calculator, the key codes for the column are 6, 7, 8, 9, 0 rather than 1 through 5, as shown in the diagram below.

Code for ⌷2nd⌷ ⌷tanh⌷ is 19.

31 (row 3 column 1 is ⌷x:y⌷)

42 (row 4 column 2 is ⌷EE⌷)

08 (number key ⌷8⌷)

65 (row 6 column 5 is ⌷−⌷)

03 (number key ⌷3⌷)

85 (row 8 column 5 is ⌷=⌷)

			TI-55	**Rows**
	sinh	cosh	tanh	CA
⌷2nd⌷	⌷sin⌷	⌷cos⌷	⌷tan⌷	⌷CLR⌷	1
	Δ%	log	10ˣ	x!	
⌷INV⌷	⌷%⌷	⌷lnx⌷	⌷eˣ⌷	⌷ˣ√y⌷	2
P→R	Mean	S. Dev	Var	Corr	
⌷x:y⌷	⌷x²⌷	⌷√x⌷	⌷1/x⌷	⌷yˣ⌷	3
Σ−	Eng	Const	π	Slope	
⌷Σ+⌷	⌷EE⌷	⌷(⌷ | ⌷)⌷	⌷÷⌷	4
Fix	Deg	Rad	Grad	Intcp	
⌷STO⌷	⌷7⌷	⌷8⌷	⌷9⌷	⌷X⌷	5
Exc	in·mm	gal·l	lb·kg	x′	
⌷RCL⌷	⌷4⌷	⌷5⌷	⌷6⌷	⌷−⌷	6
Prod	°F·°C	D·R	G·R	y′	
⌷SUM⌷	⌷1⌷	⌷2⌷	⌷3⌷	⌷+⌷	7
R/S	Rst	Lrn	Sst	DMS·DD	
⌷CE⌷	⌷0⌷	⌷·⌷	⌷+/−⌷	⌷=⌷	8

— Program —

Column numbers for	6	7	8	9	0
second functions					
Columns	1	2	3	4	5

See Appendix D in the Owner's Manual for a complete list of key codes.

The display "00 65" tells you that step 00 is ⌷−⌷ , the display "01 03" tells you that step 01 is ⌷3⌷ , etc. All of the keys used in your program are displayed with their key codes when you single step through while in the "learn mode". You can check to see if your program is entered properly using this method. If a step is not entered correctly (or you want to change it) you can enter a new keystroke at any step by simply keying it in (while in learn mode). A new keystroke will write over and replace any step that's there. (The display will then move on to the next step.)

This fairly well covers the uses of the programming keys of your calculator. (There are more details on these in your owners manual.) Before we use them again in some more examples, let's take a moment and talk about some basic techniques that can help you while you're programming.

Data Entry

Every program you write of necessity involves using some data for calculations. Because of this you need to be aware of how to enter data for your program to use. Basically there are two ways to enter data into a program: either from the display or by recalling the data from memories.

One of the simplest methods of entering data for your program is to just use the number in the display. This works well even if you need to enter more than one number, since you can always include a [2nd] [R/S] in the program to stop and allow the entry of the second value.

Another way to enter data is to store it in memories (either as part of the program or before you start the program) and then let the program recall the numbers from memory as needed for the calculation.

How you choose to arrange your program, enter data, etc., will depend on how you've evaluated your program needs and how you've programmed the solution. In other words, it depends a lot on you and your "Programming Style".

Development of Programming Style

Whether you're programming your calculator, or a large scale computer — keep one point in mind: there is no single unique programming solution to any problem. As you gain experience in programming, you'll find yourself developing your own unique style, "tricks of the trade", and favorite techniques in getting at a solution. As you begin gaining experience, it's a good idea to review your techniques periodically to be sure you're using all the power of your machine. Don't be afraid to explore new routes, try new alternatives, and experiment with new methods. Programming is an excellent exercise in clear, common sense, logical thinking that many folks enjoy (and some are quite addicted to). Your calculator is deliberately designed to allow you to get started easily, and then grow quite quickly into an expert in creating programs.

Steps in Writing a Program

As you learn more about programming, you'll begin falling into a "natural rhythm" where programming solutions will begin to suggest themselves to you as soon as you're confronted with a problem. The actual steps you'll follow in getting to a program solution will naturally depend on your personal approach, but these steps suggest one way to proceed:

1. Study the problem — gather the equations and procedures you'll need.

2. Set a destination for yourself. Determine how you'll use the program, so that when the program is complete, you'll know what to enter, what keys you'll press, and what you want to see displayed.

3. Plan the Program "Route" — Conceptualize how the program will "flow" (a flow chart or schematic diagram of the steps you'll follow may be helpful here).

4. Write down the actual program steps (or, as you gain confidence, key them right into your machine). As you go along keep careful track of what is stored in each memory. This is easy to forget and is a common source of errors and "start overs".

5. Once the program is entered, check it with known test data to be sure it's working.

6. Edit and correct as necessary.

7. Document or "write up" the program carefully to save it for future use. Once your program is working, you can press [2nd] [Rst] ,

2nd [Lrn] and then use the 2nd [Sst] key to step through the key codes and record them. This type of complete record will let you (or a friend) pick up the program at a future date and understand the program — how it works, how to use it, and how to check it to be certain it's working.

With these points in mind, let's look at another example program.

A SIMPLE PROGRAM

Write a program to solve for side C (hypotenuse) of three right triangles if sides A and B are known.

Triangle 1: $A = 5, B = 2.5, C = ?$

Triangle 2. $A = 12, B = 2.5, C = ?$

Triangle 3: $A = 4.5, B = 9, C = ?$

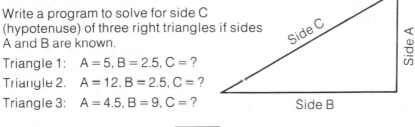

$$\sqrt{A^2 + B^2} = C$$

Looking at the equation above and the known A and B values, you can see that the program must be entered such that the A and B values can be entered from the keyboard. You can assume that the A value is in the display when you start the program. The only decision left is whether to store the B value in a memory to be recalled by the program or just place a run/stop in the program where the B value is needed. Since the B value is 2.5 for two of the three calculations, you can save some time by using the memory.

Keying in the Program

Press			Display/Comments
2nd [CA]			**0** Completely clears calculator.
2nd [Lrn]			**00 00** Enter the learn mode.
[x²] [+] [RCL]	0		**04 00** Squares A, recalls B from memory.
[x²] [=] [√x̄]			**07 00** Squares B, takes square root of $A^2 + B^2$.
2nd [R/S]			**08 00** Tells program to stop and display answer.
2nd [Rst]			**09 00** Resets program to step 00 each time program is repeated. Saves manually resetting program.
2nd [Lrn]			**0** Exit the learn mode.

Running the Program

Now run the program for the known values of A and B. But first press
[2nd] [Rst] to manually reset the program to 00 after leaving the
learn mode. If you don't, this program will begin with step 09 (which
contains no key function).

Press	Display/Comments	
[2nd] [Fix] 2	**0.00**	Fix decimal at two places.
[2nd] [Rst]	**0.00**	Reset program to step 00.
2.5 [STO] 0	**2.50**	Store B value in memory 0.
5	**5**	Enter first A value
[2nd] [R/S]	**5.59**	= C for triangle 1
12	**12**	Enter second A value, B remains same.
[2nd] [R/S]	**12.26**	= C for triangle 2
9 [STO] 0	**9.00**	Store third B value in memory 0.
4.5	**4.5**	Enter third A value.
[2nd] [R/S]	**10.06**	= C for triangle 3

Changing the Program

Now let's look at the same program using [2nd] [R/S] to stop and
enter data instead of recalling from a memory. Rather than keying in
the program again, we'll just change the program so it stops for the
B value to be entered instead of using memory 0. This change is
accomplished by using [2nd] [Sst] in the learn mode until [RCL]
(code 61) is reached in step 02. Then we'll key in a [2nd] [R/S] .

However, since there are two steps in the program (RCL 0) that
need to be replaced by one step (2nd R/S), a filler step needs to
be inserted that will not affect the program calculation. Two such
filler functions are CE and INV which when used prior to
2nd R/S will not affect the calculation. Here's how to change, or
edit, our program.

Press	**Display/Comments**
CLR 2nd Rst	**0.** Clears display and resets program to step 00.
2nd Lrn	**00 32** Enter learn mode. The x^2 key code is in step 00.
2nd Sst	**01 75** + key code.
2nd Sst	**02 61** RCL key code.
CE	**03 00** Replaced RCL with CE filler function. 0 for old memory location is now showing.
2nd R/S	**04 32** Replaced 0 with 2nd R/S x^2 key code in next step is now showing.
2nd Lrn	**0** Exit learn mode. Change complete.

Run the revised program for triangle 3.

2nd Rst	**0.00** Resets program to step 00.
4.5 2nd R/S	**20.25** Enter A value. A^2 displayed.
9	**9** Enter B value.
2nd R/S	**10.06** = C for triangle 3.

If you've been counting keystrokes during the previous programming
example, you may have noticed that programming here takes more
keystrokes than solving the problem directly on the keyboard. This
can be true for short problems requiring only two or three solutions.
However, long problems requiring a few solutions or short
problems requiring many solutions can be solved with much less
effort by using the programming feature of the calculator. We'll
continue throughout the rest of the book to show you programming
examples that apply readily to the time-saving benefits of
programming.

Measuring & Forecasting Trends

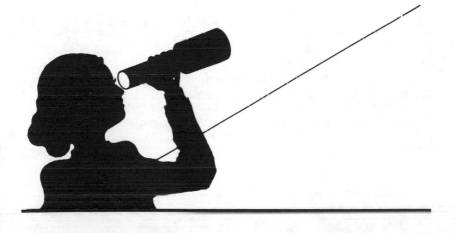

Introduction

Knowledge about (and some control over) what will happen *in the future* is an important aspect of managing any type of business enterprise *today*. The more you can predict about how prices will vary; how well a sales force will perform; how advertising will affect sales; etc., the easier it will be to make sound decisions in a variety of business situations. Knowing how well one variable will relate to another can allow you to make better things happen in your everyday life, as well as your business!

The following examples illustrate some techniques aimed at *making predictions of future performance based on past "track records"*. We'll also discuss tools for making decisions about *whether or not two variables are related,* and if so, how much you can rely on the relationship in "driving" your business. Your calculator is equipped with special keys that can make handling the math involved a cinch! These keys handle what statisticians would call the techniques of *linear regression* and *correlation*. If you're not really familiar with all the "ins and outs" of what these words mean, that's not important. What is important is that they're the names of very useful mathematical tools that your calculator makes easy to use.

Keys to Linear Regression — or, Straight Line Graphs Made Easy

The "linear regression" part of your calculator includes the ‹x:y› and ‹Σ+› keys, as well as all the second function keys on the right side of the machine labeled.

| Corr | Slope | Intcp | *x'* | *y'* |

Basically what these keys do is allow your calculator to mathematically draw the "best fitting line" through a series of data points. You just key in your data with the ‹x:y› and ‹Σ+› keys. While you're doing this, your calculator keeps up with you constantly — "drawing" the best fitting straight line through these points. The *basic* elements of how these special keys are used were discussed for you in *Chapter 1*. In this chapter we'll go through a brief review of the process with a little more detail — so you're sure you're using the keys correctly before we move on to *calculating better decisions*. (The techniques described in the chapter will allow you to make predictions on any process or operation that can be assumed to follow a straight line pattern of behavior.)

Example: Let's say you've got some data — it can be about any sort of process or operation, but it's the best "track record" you've got — and you need to make some future predictions based on it. Data such as this is often expressed in terms of pairs of numbers labeled with the letters x and y such as those tabulated below. The points could be "plotted" pictorially as shown:

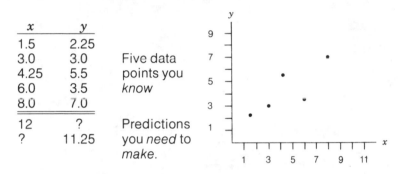

x	y	
1.5	2.25	Five data
3.0	3.0	points you
4.25	5.5	*know*
6.0	3.5	
8.0	7.0	
12	?	Predictions
?	11.25	you *need* to
		make.

Now, x and y can be any of a variety of variables with some relation between them. (Thousands of dollars of advertising vs. sales volume in hundreds of units; employees' scores on an exam vs. performance, etc.). Your task is usually to make predictions based on the data you've got. Typical things you might need to know in this case could be:

For a given x value (say $x = 12$), what will the value of y be? *or*

For what x value will y reach some specific number (say 11.25)?

You might also like to know something about how accurate the predictions are, as well as how you can make additional predictions easily at a later time.

Here's how to use your calculator to help:

Steps in Calculating Predictions and Forecasting Trends

First, enter the information you *have* (your data) as follows:
Enter each x value, push ⓧ⋮ⓨ , enter the *corresponding y value*,
then push ⓢ⁺ .
Repeat the process for all the data.
For the data tabulated in our example:

Press	**Display/Comments**
2nd CA	0
1.5 ⓧ⋮ⓨ 2.25 ⓢ⁺	**1.** Notice that the
3.0 ⓧ⋮ⓨ 3.0 ⓢ⁺	**2.** calculator keeps
4.25 ⓧ⋮ⓨ 5.5 ⓢ⁺	**3.** track of how
6.0 ⓧ⋮ⓨ 3.5 ⓢ⁺	**4.** many data points
8.0 ⓧ⋮ⓨ 7.0 ⓢ⁺	**5.** (pairs of x and y values that you enter)

As you enter the data, your calculator is storing and analyzing it.

Now, if you *need to predict a y value, for a given x value* just:
enter the x value, and press 2nd 𝒚′
In our case we need to know: for $x = 12$, what will y be?

Press	**Display/Comments**
12. 2nd 𝒚′	**8.8882025** – the y value for $x = 12$.

If you want to go the other way — that is, you have a y value and need
to know the corresponding x value:
enter the y value, then press 2nd 𝒙′ .
In our case we want to know at what x value y will reach 11.25.

Press	**Display/Comments**
11.25 2nd 𝒙′	**15.79358** – the x value for $y = 11.25$

To get a picture of *how well the data correlates*
press 2nd Corr . This displays the *correlation coefficient* for
the line.

In our case:

Press	**Display/Comments**
2nd Corr	**0.8097825**

About the Correlation Coefficient

The [2nd] [Corr] key sequence displays the *correlation coefficient* of the two sets of data (x's and y's). A value close to plus 1 indicates a high positive correlation and a value close to minus 1 indicates a high negative correlation. A value of zero indicates that the two sets of data are not related.

For example: Suppose your company gives two tests to new employees—*Test A* and *Test B*. If there is a high positive correlation between the two tests, then you can predict that an employee who scores high (or low) on *Test A* will also score high (or low) on *Test B*. On the other hand, if there is a high negative correlation between the two tests, you can predict that an employee who scores high (or low) on *Test A* will score low (or high) on *Test B*. If there is no correlation (correlation coefficient equals 0), then you can say nothing about how an employee's performance on *Test A* relates to his or her performance on *Test B*.

Slope and Intercept

To find out more about the line, press [2nd] [Slope] and [2nd] [Intcp] to display the slope and intercept of the line.

Press	Display/Comments
[2nd] [Slope]	0.6225775
[2nd] [Intcp]	1.4172723

The slope of the line is the ratio of its "rise" to its "run", while the intercept is where it crosses the y axis. Any straight line may be expressed as an equation most commonly written in the form:
$$y = mx + b$$
Where m is the slope value and b is the intercept value.

Using your calculated values you could then write an equation for the line best fitting your data as follows:
$$y = (.62)x + 1.42$$
(Where we've rounded off the slope and intercept)

You could then use this equation to predict a y value for any selected x value with a simple calculation later on, without having to re-enter the data each time.

Putting It All Together

So, using the linear regression and correlation keys can give you quite a bit of information about (and analysis of) your data. To use the calculator to do this, you just:

Enter each x value and press 『x⇄y』 .

Enter each y value and press 『Σ+』 .

The calculator mathematically draws the "best fitting line" for your data points — and you can use the information about this line to predict:

Given any x value, what is the corresponding y value?
(enter the value of x, press 『2nd』 『y'』 .)

Given any y value, what is the corresponding x value?
(enter y, press 『2nd』 『x'』 .)

You can also get an idea of how well the data correlates.

(Press 『2nd』 『Corr』 — the closer the display reads to plus or minus 1, the better the correlation.)

To calculate the slope and intercept of the line:

press 『2nd』 『Slope』 and 『2nd』 『Intcp』 .

The following diagram illustrates all of this for you:

After entering the x, y coordinates of the known values

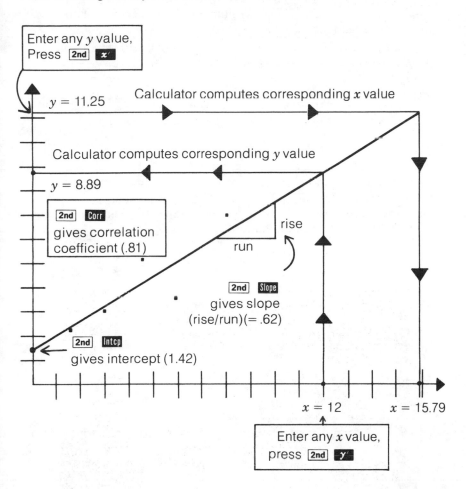

Enter any y value,
Press [2nd] [x']

$y = 11.25$ Calculator computes corresponding x value

Calculator computes corresponding y value

$y = 8.89$

[2nd] [Corr]
gives correlation
coefficient (.81)

rise

run

[2nd] [Slope]
gives slope
(rise/run)(= .62)

[2nd] [Intcp]
gives intercept (1.42)

$x = 12$ $x = 15.79$

Enter any x value,
press [2nd] [y']

The rest of this chapter covers a few examples of how these
procedures can be helpful in calculating better decisions.

Predicting Sales from Advertising (LINEAR REGRESSION)

Let's say your company has recently started advertising in a new medium (say a series of magazines), on a weekly basis. The marketing manager has a record of the amount spent on advertising each week (x) and the corresponding sales volume (y) and there seems to be a fairly good relationship. His question of you is: what would the expected sales volume be if $4750 is spent on magazine advertising next week?

Amount Spent on Advertising (x)	Weekly Sales Volume (y)
$1000	101,000
$1250	116,000
$1500	165,000
$2000	209,000
$2500	264,000
$4750	???

Target: You want to predict what will happen, in unit sales (y), if your advertising budget (x) is increased to $4750 — using the "best straight line" approximation.

Tools: You'll be using the *linear regression* feature of your calculator to help predict the result. First, you'll be *entering your data:*

Enter $ in advertising:
press [x:y]
Enter corresponding unit sales:
press [Σ+]

To make your prediction you'll enter your trial advertising $ value, and to find the predicted result just press [2nd] [y']

PREDICTING SALES
FROM ADVERTISING
(LINEAR REGRESSION)

MEASURING &
FORECASTING
TRENDS

2

You'll note a slight pause when you press the y' key — before the result is displayed. That's because your calculator has the chore of handling the linear regression calculation (not you). Here's the formula for what it's doing:

$$y' = \left[\frac{\dfrac{\Sigma x_i \, \Sigma y_i}{N} - \Sigma x_i y_i}{\dfrac{(\Sigma x_i)^2}{N} - \Sigma x_i{}^2} \right] \times \text{(your "}x\text{" value)}$$

$$+ \left\{ \frac{\Sigma y_i}{N} - \left[\frac{\dfrac{\Sigma x_i \, \Sigma y_i}{N} - \Sigma x_i y_i}{\dfrac{(\Sigma x_i)^2}{N} - \Sigma x_i{}^2} \right] \left(\frac{\Sigma x_i}{N} \right) \right\}$$

(Think of the "fun" you'd have doing this calculation yourself!)

(To find out about how well your data correlates to a straight line, you can press [2nd] **Corr** to display the correlation coefficient. A value near one means a fairly good linear correlation.)

Keying It In: First, enter the data:

Press	Display/Comments
[2nd] **CA**	**0** Clears entire machine.
[2nd] **FIX** 2	**0.00** Sets display to read out 2
Enter the 5 data points:	decimal places.
1000 [x:y] 101,000 [Σ+]	**1.00** Calculator
1250 [x:y] 116,000 [Σ+]	**2.00** displays the
1500 [x:y] 165,000 [Σ+]	**3.00** number of
2000 [x:y] 209,000 [Σ+]	**4.00** (x,y) points
2500 [x:y] 264,000 [Σ+]	**5.00** entered
	Now, to find the y value
	for $x = \$4750$
4750 [2nd] y'	**514672.41**

Based on the best straight line approximation, the projected weekly sales volume for $4750 spent on advertising is 514,672.41 units.

Now to check out how good an estimate you and your calculator made:

Press	Display/Comments
[2nd] **Corr**	**0.99**

Nearly perfect positive correlation!

PREDICTING SALES
FROM ADVERTISING
(LINEAR REGRESSION)

MEASURING &
FORECASTING
TRENDS

2

Decision Time: You're now in a position to make predictions about your future sales based on advertising. Your correlation coefficient seems to indicate that the prediction will be a good one — but remember the total number of data points you're working with is small — you have only 5 points upon which to predict the future. As it turns out — there's a way to further analyze your correlation that allows you to take the number of data points into account (see *Going Further* section).

So, to get down to a decision at this point — you might take a look at the increased cost, weigh that against the increase in sales that you predict will result — and see if it's "worth it".

Press	Display/Comments
CLR	**0**
4750 ─ 2500 ═	**2250.00** Amount of advertising increase.
514672.41 ─ 264,000 ═	**250672.41** Increase in unit sales predicted.

"Cause and Effect"

Note an important point here. Strictly speaking all we've shown in this example is that a definite *relationship* exists between advertising and sales. Be careful about drawing conclusions about *cause and effect*. In this case, you can probably be pretty sure that your advertising is pushing your sales up — but in other cases, the "cause and effect" relation may not be so obvious. Two variables that are related to a *third* can show a relation to each other — without a "cause and effect" relation between them.

For example, you may have data on children that relates manual dexterity (let's say the time to finish a simple jigsaw puzzle) directly to mathematical ability (performance on a math test). The relation may show quite a good correlation coefficient. It may turn out, however, that *age* is the dominant factor "driving" the variables. Further analysis may show that the older children naturally display both better manual coordination and mathematical skill — and that if your sample is restructured to include only children of the same age — an entirely different relationship may result. So be careful about how you apply your results in making decisions. Consider the makeup of your sample and exactly what you're measuring and testing.

PREDICTING SALES
FROM ADVERTISING
(LINEAR REGRESSION)

MEASURING &
FORECASTING
TRENDS

2

Going Further: Correlation Factor Validity

As we briefly mentioned — in this example you're predicting the future based on only five data points from the past — and that's not much to go on. In general, the less data you have to go on, the more "chancy" your prediction will be. As it turns out there's a quick way to get a measure of how valid your correlation factor is under different data conditions. (As a general rule, if you don't have much data — unless your correlation factor is quite close to plus or minus one — you can't be too sure of it.)

One procedure for a quick check on the validity of your correlation coefficient is as follows:
a) Decide how sure or valid you'd like (or need) the correlation coefficient to be — say 95%.
b) Locate the r_{test} (test correlation coefficient) value from the table at the end of this chapter — for the degree of certainty you've selected, and the number of samples you have to work with — (don't worry about the "degrees of freedom" column in the table for now).
c) If your calculated correlation coefficient is *greater than* r_{test}, you can be certain (to the degree selected) that your straight line approximation is valid.

In our case, the calculated correlation coefficient is 0.99. We compare this to the r_{test} value; at 95% certainty for 5 samples (find this value in the tables):

$$r_{test} = .878$$

Since our correlation coefficient is greater than r_{test}, we can assume that our correlation coefficient is valid, to a 95% degree of certainty. (Being 95% certain of a conclusion means that 95 times out of 100 you will be correct.)

Stock Dividend Projections (TREND LINE ANALYSIS)

You'll find many instances when your data is collected in the form of a series of yearly figures—and your job is to predict what will happen in years to come. This type of prediction involves what statisticians call "trend line analysis"—which is really just a special type of linear regression. Your calculator has features that make trend line analysis easy.

Example: A stock that you've been keeping your eye on has reported the following earnings per share during the past few years:

> $1.52 in 1972
> 1.35 in 1973
> 1.53 in 1974
> 2.17 in 1975
> 3.60 in 1976

You'd like to predict the earnings per share for the next three years. You'd also like to know in what year you could expect the earnings per share to reach $6.50.

Target: You wish to enter the data you *have* into your calculator, and then use trend line analysis to make predictions. You'd also like some feeling as to how well the two sets of data are correlated.

Tools: First, you'll enter your data, using the 🔲 and 🔲 keys. In this case the "*x*" values are a series of years *in sequence,* and the "*y*" values are the stock dividends recorded for each year. (Data for a series of successive years is common for trend line analysis situations.)

Now—here's an important feature—for Trend Line Analysis your calculator will *automatically* add 1 to the *x* variable for you. This means that:

> You can enter the first *x* value (say the first year, 1972) and press 🔲 , then enter a *y* value (say $1.52 earnings per share) and press 🔲 . The first data point is entered.

Then:
> You can enter the second data point by just entering the y value (in our case $1.35) and hitting ⎡Σ+⎤ . The calculator will automatically handle the x variable for you—incrementing it by 1.

This will come in handy whenever you're analyzing data from successive years—or whenever your x variable is going up in increments of 1.

After your data is entered:
To make predictions on earnings for future years; just enter the year and press ⎡2nd⎤ **y′**
To predict in what year a certain level of earnings per share will be reached:
> Enter the earnings and press ⎡2nd⎤ **x′**

To see how well the two sets of data correlate: Press ⎡2nd⎤ **Corr**

To check on the validity of the correlation—compare your correlation factor to the "r_{test}" value in the table at the end of this chapter.

Keying It In:

Press	**Display/Comments**
⎡2nd⎤ **CA**	**0.** This clears the display and memories.
⎡2nd⎤ **Fix** 2	**0.00** This sets the display to read out only two decimal places.

Now enter your data:
1972 ⎡x:y⎤ 1.52 ⎡Σ+⎤

1.00 Note: the calculator will

1.35 ⎡Σ+⎤   **2.00** increase the value by 1

1.53 ⎡Σ+⎤   **3.00** automatically unless

2.17 ⎡Σ+⎤   **4.00** another value is entered.

3.60 ⎡Σ+⎤   **5.00** The years are automatically "passing by" for you!

Decision Time: Now, to predict the earnings for future years (future y values) just key in the year, and press [2nd] [y'] :

1977 [2nd] [y']

3.53 Dividends of $3.53 per share are projected for 1977

1978 [2nd] [y']
1979 [2nd] [y']

4.03 for 1978
4.52 for 1979

You can now make decisions based on the pattern of growth you're watching — or go on to predict when the earnings per share will reach a specified value. For example, to calculate when the earnings will reach $6.50 (if the earning trend continues) — you just enter the 6.50 and press [2nd] [x']

6.50 [2nd] [x']

1982.97 or about 1983.

Going Further: If you'd like to see how well the two sets of data are correlated just press:

[2nd] [Corr]

0.85

You can get an idea as to how "valid" the correlation coefficient is by checking in the table at the end of the chapter. First, find the line with the same number of samples you have here (5). Now — scan across to the right at the "r_{test}" values and find the *first one that's larger* than your r value (.85). (You should find the value .878). You can now glance up to the certainty values at the top of the table to draw a conclusion: you can be about 90-95% sure that this correlation coefficient is "valid".

Relating Job Performance to Test Score

(ESTABLISHING CORRELATION)

In this example we'll use the linear regression feature of your calculator, in particular the *correlation* feature (**2nd** **Corr**) to help make a decision on *whether or not two variables are related*. It may often appear that one factor in your business life is related to another — but just how closely they really "track" is often unclear. With your calculator you can get a more accurate picture of just how much relation there is between two variables.

Example: Test Scores vs Performance

Let's say your sales manager is spending a considerable sum on a test for prospective sales employees. You'd like to see if this test is actually telling you anything about how well the employee will function in the field. Does a higher test score mean superior sales performance? How strong a *correlation* is there between these two factors in your business?

Let's say you have samples of the test scores for 10 employees, along with records on sales performance expressed as the percentage of the time that each employee exceeded his or her weekly sales goals last year. The data is tabulated below:

Employee	Employee Test Score (x)	Employee Sales Performance (y)
Jerry	5	10
Ross	13	30
Joe	8	30
Ralph	10	40
Mary	15	60
Gary	20	50
Dean	4	20
Carole	16	60
Ted	18	50
Alice	6	20

RELATING JOB PERFORMANCE
TO TEST SCORE
(ESTABLISHING CORRELATION)

MEASURING &
FORECASTING
TRENDS

2

Target: Determine if there is a genuine relationship between test scores and sales performance. If so, what is the relationship, and can you get a feel for how reliable it is?

Tools: Your calculator's linear regression feature can easily apply some high powered statistical mathematics to this problem for you.
First: Enter your data with the $\boxed{x{:}y}$ and $\boxed{\Sigma+}$ keys.
Then: Study the correlation coefficient (r) by pressing $\boxed{2nd}$ $\boxed{Corr}$, and consulting the "r_{test}" table at the end of this chapter.

Keying It In: Enter the data and determine the correlation coefficient.

Press	Display/Comments
$\boxed{2nd}$ $\boxed{CA}$	**0** Clear entire machine, including memories.
$\boxed{2nd}$ $\boxed{Fix}$ 2	**0.00** Set display to read-out to 2 decimal places.
5 $\boxed{x{:}y}$ 10 $\boxed{\Sigma+}$	**1.00**
13 $\boxed{x{:}y}$ 30 $\boxed{\Sigma+}$	**2.00**
8 $\boxed{x{:}y}$ 30 $\boxed{\Sigma+}$	**3.00**
10 $\boxed{x{:}y}$ 40 $\boxed{\Sigma+}$	**4.00**
15 $\boxed{x{:}y}$ 60 $\boxed{\Sigma+}$	**5.00**
20 $\boxed{x{:}y}$ 50 $\boxed{\Sigma+}$	**6.00**
4 $\boxed{x{:}y}$ 20 $\boxed{\Sigma+}$	**7.00**
16 $\boxed{x{:}y}$ 60 $\boxed{\Sigma+}$	**8.00**
18 $\boxed{x{:}y}$ 50 $\boxed{\Sigma+}$	**9.00**
6 $\boxed{x{:}y}$ 20 $\boxed{\Sigma+}$	**10.00**
	To find the correlation factor:
$\boxed{2nd}$ $\boxed{Corr}$	**0.87** = r

RELATING JOB PERFORMANCE
TO TEST SCORE
(ESTABLISHING CORRELATION)

MEASURING &
FORECASTING
TRENDS

2

Decision Time:

The correlation factor of 0.87 tells you that there is a pretty good relationship between the test scores and the indicator for employee performance that you're using.

To get a general feel for how valid this correlation factor is – glance at the table at the end of this chapter. Find the line for the number of samples you've got (in this case 10) and examine the "r_{test}" values listed to the right. Your value for r (the correlation coefficient – 0.87) falls between .765 and .872 listed on the table – so you can be between 99% and 99.9% sure it's a "valid" correlation coefficient – there is a definite relationship between these variables.

Going Further: Future Predictions

Using the data you've got in your calculator, you can now go on and predict employee performance for any given test score. Just key in the score (x) value and press [2nd] [y'] . Some examples:

Press	Display/Comments
7 [2nd] [y']	**24.92**
25 [2nd] [y']	**73.23**
30 [2nd] [y']	**86.65**

If you wish to make *future predictions* again at some later date, you can easily write down the *equation of the line* your calculator has "drawn" through your data using the [2nd] [Slope] and [2nd] [Intcp] key sequences:

[2nd] [Slope]	**2.68**	slope value (m)
[2nd] [Intcp]	**6.14**	intercept value (b)

The equation of any straight line can be expressed as:

$$y = mx + b$$

$y = $ (Slope) $\times (x) + $ (Intcp); so in this case the line is given by

$$y = 2.68\,x + 6.14$$

So, if at some future date you wish to make a prediction – you only need note the slope and intercept values. If an employee then scores a 24.2 on his test, you can substitute that result for x in the equation for the line to predict his or her performance:

[2nd] [CA]	**0** Clear machine
2.68 [X] 24.2	
[+] 6.14 [=]	**70.996** – a good prospect for field sales!

RELATING JOB PERFORMANCE
TO TEST SCORE
(ESTABLISHING CORRELATION)

MEASURING &
FORECASTING
TRENDS

2

How to Use "r_{test}" Table for Correlation Coefficients

Find the number of samples you have in the left hand column, and scan across to the right — comparing the values of r_{test} listed in the table to your calculated correlation coefficient. Find the values of r_{test} that your correlation coefficient fits "in between" and scan upward to read the "degree of certainty" limits for your coefficient. If your correlation coefficient is too small for you to find in the table, then you're less than 80% sure of its validity.

The values in this table are from the formula:

$$r_{test} = \left(\frac{t^2}{t^2 + df}\right)^{1/2}$$ where df = the degrees of freedom, and t is the t value for df from table C in the *Appendix*.

Example: For 15 samples, a correlation coefficient of .525 can be considered between 95% and 99% "valid".

RELATING JOB PERFORMANCE
TO TEST SCORE
(ESTABLISHING CORRELATION)

MEASURING &
FORECASTING
TRENDS

2

Table of "r_{test}" Values — Test Values for Correlation Coefficient

# of Samples	(df) degrees of Freedom	80%	90%	95%	99%	99.9%
3	1	0.951	.988	.997	1.000	1.000
4	2	0.800	.900	.950	.990	.999
5	3	0.687	.805	.878	.959	.991
6	4	0.608	.729	.811	.917	.974
7	5	0.551	.669	.755	.875	.951
8	6	0.507	.621	.707	.834	.925
9	7	0.472	.582	.666	.798	.898
10	8	0.443	.549	.632	.765	.872
11	9	0.419	.521	.602	.735	.847
12	10	0.398	.497	.576	.708	.823
13	11	0.380	.476	.553	.684	.801
14	12	0.365	.457	.532	.661	.780
15	13	0.351	.441	.514	.641	.760
16	14	0.338	.426	.497	.623	.742
17	15	0.327	.412	.482	.606	.725
18	16	0.317	.400	.468	.590	.708
19	17	0.308	.389	.456	.575	.693
20	18	0.299	.378	.444	.561	.679
21	19	0.291	.369	.433	.549	.665
22	20	0.284	.360	.423	.537	.652
23	21	0.277	.352	.413	.526	.640
24	22	0.271	.344	.404	.515	.629
25	23	0.265	.337	.396	.505	.618
26	24	0.260	.330	.388	.496	.607
27	25	0.255	.323	.381	.487	.597
28	26	0.250	.317	.374	.479	.588
29	27	0.245	.311	.367	.471	.579
30	28	0.241	.306	.361	.463	.570
31	29	0.237	.301	.355	.456	.562
32	30	0.233	.296	.349	.449	.554
42	40	0.202	.257	.304	.393	.490
62	60	0.165	.211	.250	.325	.408
122	120	0.117	.150	.178	.232	.294

Testing Claims

Introduction

Many times in your business (or everyday life) you're forced into making decisions (buy/not buy — accept/not accept) about a *large lot* or *quantity* of items. Time and expense usually allow you only to examine and test a few *samples* of the large population you have to decide on. (This is often the case in an "incoming quality control" operation, for example.)

Whenever you're in this situation — deciding about a large *population* based on a smaller *sample* — a certain amount of *uncertainty* is always present. The sample is giving you some information to be sure — the key is using your sample data wisely. When a manufacturer *claims* that a lot of goods meets a certain specification — data from your sample can be used to test that claim to a *specified degree of certainty*. The examples in this chapter are designed to show you how — and how your calculator can help.

In this chapter we'll get into the examination and analysis of data from samples, and the hows and whys of relating that data to larger populations. We'll proceed step-by-step through the analysis of several typical case situations with some sample data — so that you will hopefully be able to apply the tools illustrated to your own analysis situations. Some fairly "high powered" statistical methods are involved here, but with your calculator keeping tabs on the mathematics, you'll be surprised at how the implementations of these techniques get simplified.

First Things First

In most of the examples we'll be considering in this chapter the following situation is addressed:

A manufacturer (grower/supplier, etc.) makes a claim about a particular specification for a shipment of goods he's just delivered. This *claim* usually is expressed as a *mean value* for the population:

"The mean weight of product in these containers is 510 grams."
"The mean lifetime of these batteries under standard load conditions is 180 hours...."

You usually get a chance to test a sample of these parts to see if they're O.K.

The first thing to do is to take as large a sample as possible and examine the mean value of the specification for the sample, as well as its standard deviation. Your Advanced Professional Calculator has keys that make this quite easy. Just take your measured sample data and enter it with the ∑+ key. The 2nd Mean and 2nd S.Dev. key sequences will give you the mean and standard deviation of your sample data and a "first step" in your decision. Is the mean close to the claimed value? Is the standard deviation large or small?

A large standard deviation indicates a *highly varying* value for the parameter you're examining — and may be enough reason for you to reject the shipment immediately! The rest of this chapter tells you "how to use statistical inferences" in calculator decision making based on your sample results. Focus on these important concepts: the *population* refers to the entire set of items being tested, the *sample* is a part of the population that's been "picked out" for test. You'll be making decisions about the *population*, based on *sample* data, and the *level of certainty* you decide.

Mean Weight of Aerosol Dispensers

Testing the manufacturer's claim — with concern about *both* upper and lower limits:

Here's an example situation that calls for a decision about a population based on a sample. Let's say a large shipment (population) of aerosol cans of insecticide has just arrived at your receiving dock. The manufacturer claims that the cans contain, on the average, 510 grams of insecticide each. Maybe you usually just take this fact at face value — but this time you'd like to be sure that he's meeting this claim.

You're concerned about this problem for two reasons — these particular cans don't work properly if they're overfull; and you're getting gypped if they're less than full. The ideal case is when each can contains exactly 510 grams — and you're concerned about the manufacturer meeting this "spec." — *both on the high and low end.* (This is what's called a "two-sided" or "two-tailed" decision-making process.)

You have a technician measure the weight of 40 cans (the sample) and tabulate the data for you. With a quick calculation on your calculator you found:

    The mean sample weight is 508.75 g (usually labeled $\bar{x}$)
    The sample standard deviation (labeled s_x) is 19.97g

The decision — is the manufacturer meeting his claim? Should you accept the shipment or reject it? Can the sample data give you a little more to go on? It can — read on!

Target: Let's say you want to be 95% sure that the manufacturer has not met his claim before you reject the shipment. Your target here is to get as much information as you can about the population, based on the data you have from the sample.

Tools: Here your *sample size* is over 30 items — which statisticians generally agree to as an informal boundary between "large" and "small" samples. For your "large" sample of 40 items you may assume that the *sample standard deviation* (s_x) is a pretty good estimate of *the population standard deviation* (usually labeled with the lower case Greek letter sigma, σ).

This fact often allows you to immediately reach some important conclusions. Most manufacturing processes deviate from the specified or target value in a "normal" way. This means that the population values can often be considered to follow the normal curve. If this is the case, then about 95% of the cans will be within ±2 standard deviations of the mean. The sample standard deviation of 19.97 implies a range of ±2 (19.97) (± about 40 grams) for about 95% of the cans. If, in your case, a ±40 grams variation in the weight of the cans is by itself unacceptable, you may need to reject the cans based on this standard deviation value alone.

If the standard deviation value *is* acceptable to you—you now need to proceed to a little more complete analysis: There's a tool from statistics that lets you:
a) Select a degree of certainty for your decision to accept or reject—say 95%.
b) With a straightforward calculation you can now establish a *range* within which the population mean (labeled μ) lies, to the degree of certainty you selected. The formula for this range is:

$$\text{Range for } \mu \text{ at degree of certainty you select} = \bar{x} \pm \frac{\sigma}{\sqrt{n}} z$$

In this formula $\bar{x}$ is your sample mean, n is the number of samples, and z is the "z score" for the degree of certainty you select. This "z score" is found in Table A in the *Appendix*—from column II where z values for checking *both* upper and lower levels are tabulated. If you check in that table—column II reads a z value of 1.96 at 95% degree of certainty.

So summarizing:

From Table A: $z = 1.96$

$\sigma = s_x = 19.97$ (for large samples only, $n > 30$)

$n = 40$

$\bar{x} = 508.75,$

and you need to

Evaluate: $\bar{x} \pm \dfrac{\sigma}{\sqrt{n}} z.$

Keying It In: A good way to begin this calculation is to evaluate the last term $\dfrac{\sigma}{\sqrt{n}} z$, and store it in memory 1.

Press	Display/Comments
Press	**Display/Comments**
[2nd] [CA]	**0** Clear all memories and registers
[2nd] [Fix] 2	**0.00** Set calculator to display only 2 decimal places.
19.97 [÷] 40 [√x] [X]	This evaluates $\dfrac{\sigma}{\sqrt{n}} z$
1.96 [=] [STO] 1	**6.19** and stores it
	Next, evaluate $\bar{x} + \dfrac{\sigma}{\sqrt{n}} z$:
[+] 508.75 [=]	**514.94**
	Evaluate $\bar{x} - \dfrac{\sigma}{\sqrt{n}} z$:
508.75 [−] [RCL] 1 [=]	**502.56**

Manufacturer's claimed value of 510g falls inside these limits — accept!

$$\bar{x} - \frac{\sigma}{\sqrt{n}} z \qquad\qquad 510\text{ g} \qquad\qquad \bar{x} + \frac{\sigma}{\sqrt{n}} z$$

Range of the Population Mean

502.56 g   514.94 g

Your *sample* is telling you that the *population* mean is somewhere between these two numbers, with 95% certainty.

Decision Time: You now have a better picture of what your sample is telling you about the shipment. You've got two values; 502.56 grams and 514.94 grams, and now you can say with 95% certainty that the mean weight value for the shipment (the whole population) lies in between these two values. Since the manufacturer's claimed weight value of 510 grams falls within these limits, as far as you can tell from your sample, he's met his claim. Based on this analysis — you'd *accept* the shipment of aerosol cans.

The analysis you've just done is summarized for you here:

a) First, get as large a sample as possible and measure it — calculate the sample mean $(\bar{x})$ and standard deviation (s_x).

b) Decide on the degree of certainty you need and calculate the *predicted range for the population mean* with the formula below:

$$(\text{Range for } \mu) = \bar{x} \pm \frac{\sigma}{\sqrt{n}} z$$

(Remember you find z from column II in Table A for the degree of certainty you select.) For samples with over 30 items, you can approximate σ with s_x.

c) If the manufacturer's claim value falls *inside* the range, accept — and vice versa.

Further Notes: When selecting the degree of certainty for a problem, it is important to realize how the statistical process works. The amount of information you have in your sample does not change. If you select a very high degree of certainty, then what you are certain about is less definite. (Got that?)

Here's an example: A mechanic looks at your car and tells you that he is pretty sure that it will cost about $80 to $100 to fix it. If you tell him that he has to be 99.9% sure of his estimate, he will probably estimate a wider range, say $50 to $200. If the situation you are investigating demands more certainty about a smaller range, then you may need to take a larger sample.

Mean Battery Lifetime

Testing a manufacturer's claim — with concern about meeting minimum specifications only:

In this example let's say you're manufacturing an electronic product into which you put a battery. A manufacturer has just shipped you 5000 of them, and he claims the mean lifetime for this shipment (population) is 180 hours. In this case, you want to check on the manufacturer's claim, but *what's critical to your decision* to accept the shipment is that the mean lifetime of the shipment of batteries is (as near as you can tell) no *less* than 180 hours. You don't really care if the batteries have a longer than 180 hour life. (In fact, this would make you very happy.) You're really just concerned about checking the "low side" of their performance. (This is what's called a "one-sided" or "one-tailed" decision process.)

To test the population of 5000 (N), you have a technician select a sample (n) of 100 batteries and measure their average lifetime under standard load conditions. (Since this test ruins the batteries — you decide you can't afford a much larger sample than 100 items.) Your technician finds out that the sample mean lifetime ($\bar{x}$) is 175 hours, with a sample standard deviation (s_x) of 18 hours. Your decision: accept or reject the shipment?

Actually — you already have quite a bit of information to go on. First of all, since your sample of 100 batteries qualifies as a "large" one (n > 30), the *sample* standard deviation (s_x) is considered to be equal to the *population* standard deviation (σ). So you really have an immediate decision to make: is the standard deviation of the shipment acceptable to you? In this case, $\sigma = 18$ hours. Let's say that you *can* accept this variability in the shipment. Now you need to make a judgment about the *population* mean (μ). Your sample mean ($\bar{x}$) is 175 hours. How can you use this information to draw a conclusion about the population mean lifetime?

Target: You need to make a decision about whether or not to accept the shipment, based on the sample data, and let's say you want to be *95% certain* that you don't reject good batteries. Your primary concern is that the battery life be *not much less than* 180 hours — if the average life is longer than this, fine!

Tools: There's a formula from statistics that allows you to calculate, from your sample data a *range* in which the population mean will lie. With this *range* you know, based on your sample data and degree of certainty you select, an upper and a lower limit for the *actual* population mean. The formula is:

$$\text{Range for population mean} = \bar{x} \pm \left[\frac{(N-n)}{(N-1)}\right]^{\frac{1}{2}} \frac{\sigma}{\sqrt{n}} z$$

(This formula may look complex — but it's easy to evaluate on your calculator.)

In this case: $\bar{x}$ is the sample mean lifetime = 175 hours
N is the population size = 5000
n is the sample size = 100
σ is the standard deviation of the population, which in this case can be approximated by s_x (= 18 hours)
    and
z is the z value found from Appendix Table A, for the degree of certainty you select (here 95%), taken from column I — since you will reject based on only one boundary in this case. (This is called a "one-sided" or "one-tailed" test.)
In our case z = 1.65

A note here: In this formula the expression $\left[\frac{(N-n)}{(N-1)}\right]^{\frac{1}{2}}$

is a factor which allows for the fact that when you test the batteries in the sample, you *remove* them from the population and can't return them after the test. This removal of sample items strictly speaking affects the "randomness" of your selection — and this "factor" corrects for this fact.

Keying It In: In doing this calculation, first evaluate the quantity

$$\left[\frac{(N-n)}{(N-1)}\right]^{\frac{1}{2}} \frac{\sigma}{\sqrt{n}} z$$ and store it. Then go on to complete the calculation.

Press	Display/Comments
2nd **CA**	**0** Clear entire calculator.
2nd **Fix** 2	**0.00** Set calculator to display 2 decimal places.
((5000 − 100)	**4900.00**
÷ (5000 − 1)	**4999.00**
) √x̄ X 18 ÷ 100	
√x̄ X 1.65 = STO 1	**2.94** Now add $\bar{x}$
+ 175 =	**177.94** Upper limit
175 − RCL 1 =	**172.06** Lower limit

Decision Time. Here you are predicting that the population mean actually has a value somewhere between 172.06 and 177.94 — and what you really want to focus your attention on here is that you now

know from your sample (with 95% certainty) that the population mean is *not greater than 177.94*. So, based on your sample data, the battery mean lifetime *is* less than 180 hours, and based on this analysis you'd reject the shipment (or talk with your vendor about correcting the problem).

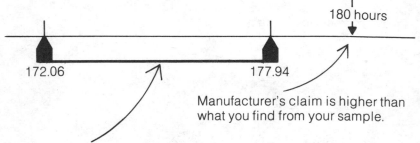

180 hours

172.06   177.94

Manufacturer's claim is higher than what you find from your sample.

Actual value of the population mean is predicted to be in this range — lower than the 180 hour lifetime you need, (and claimed by manufacturer).

Checking on Tint in Paint Mix

Testing a claim using data from a *small sample;* with concern about *both* upper and lower limits:

In this example you're doing your own check on a formulating process in a paint manufacturing operation. Specifically — you're checking on the amount of red dye being mixed into 5 gallon containers of "rose" colored paint. The process specification calls for 15.5 ounces of red tint in each can. You select a random sample of 8 cans, and through analysis, find the tint content to be:

15.2 oz	15.8 oz
15.0 oz	16.1 oz
15.7 oz	15.6 oz
15.9 oz	15.9 oz

(Let's say the analysis is expensive — so you're limited to this small sample quantity.) Your decision in this case — should you stop the manufacturing and adjust the process, or are things O.K.?

Target: You want to get as much information as you can about the population mean for the amount of red tint, based on data from the small sample you have to work with. To do this you can use a

 statistical technique especially designed to handle the "small sample" situation. This technique allows you to calculate a *predicted range* of values that the population mean (μ) will fall into, with a degree of certainty you select.

This predicted range of values can form the basis for your decision. If your calculated range of values *includes* the specification value of 15.5 oz you don't have enough indication of trouble to "stop the line." If the range of values you calculate from your sample data does *not* include your specification value, however, you can be sure (to the degree of certainty you selected) that you've got a problem and an adjustment should be made. Also, note in this case that you're concerned about both "limits" on the amount of tint — too much will give you a color that's too red, while too little tint will provide too weak a color.

Tools: Since your sample size in this case is *less than 30,* it falls into the "small" sample category and some statistical methods especially suited to this situation should be used. To use these tools:

First, decide on a degree of certainty you need for the decision — let's say 90% in this case.

Then, calculate the predicted range for the mean tint (population value) using the formula below:

$$\text{Predicted Range for Population Mean} = \bar{x} \pm \frac{s_x}{\sqrt{n}} t$$

where $\bar{x}$ is the mean value for your sample

s_x is the sample standard deviation

n is the size of the sample
and

t is a value found from Table C in the Appendix:
- for the degree of certainty you select (90%)
- and the number of *degrees of freedom* for the problem, (df). In this case:
  $$df = n - 1 = 7.$$
- checking in Table C — you'll find a t value of 1.895

To find the sample mean ($\bar{x}$) and sample standard deviation (s_x), you can use special keys on your calculator.

Keying It In: First, clear your machine and enter the sample data with the $\boxed{\Sigma +}$ key:

Press		Display/Comments
2nd CA		**0** Clear entire machine
2nd Fix 2		**0.00** Set display to read out 2 decimal places
15.2 $\boxed{\Sigma +}$		**1.00** Display keeps track of
15.0 $\boxed{\Sigma +}$		**2.00** the number of data
15.7 $\boxed{\Sigma +}$		**3.00** entries.
15.9 $\boxed{\Sigma +}$		**4.00**
15.8 $\boxed{\Sigma +}$		**5.00**
16.1 $\boxed{\Sigma +}$		**6.00**
15.6 $\boxed{\Sigma +}$		**7.00**
15.9 $\boxed{\Sigma +}$		**8.00**

Now you can, with only a couple of keystrokes, calculate the sample mean and standard deviation:

2nd Mean	**15.65**	The sample mean, $\bar{x}$
2nd S.Dev.	**0.37**	The sample standard deviation, s_x

At this point you already have quite a bit of information. The sample mean looks "pretty close" to 15.5, and the standard deviation is low — indicating that there's a relatively low "spread" to your measured sample red tint values. But remember — your sample is a small one — and you need to make an important decision about a much larger population based on it. This is where the statistical method can be helpful. Now go on to calculate the predicted range of the population mean (μ).

Predicted Range for $\mu = \bar{x} \pm \dfrac{s_x}{\sqrt{n}} t$

Now you know that $\bar{x} = 15.65$ $n = 8$
$\qquad\qquad s_x = 0.37$ $t = 1.895$

Begin by calculating $\dfrac{s_x}{\sqrt{n}} t$

Press

2nd CA
2nd Fix 2

0.37 ÷ 8 √x ×
1.895 = STO 1

+ 15.65 =

15.65 − RCL 1 =

Display/Comments

0   Clear entire machine
0.00 Set display to 2
      decimal places

0.25 Now add this to $\bar{x}$ to find
      upper range limit:

15.90 $= \bar{x} + \dfrac{s_x}{\sqrt{n}} t$

15.40 $= \bar{x} - \dfrac{s_x}{\sqrt{n}} t$

Decision Time:

15.50 oz amount of red tint specified

15.40	15.90

Your sample states that with 90% certainty the population mean lies between these two values.

From your small sample of 8 cans you can state that with 90% certainty the *population mean* value for the red tint is between 15.4 and 15.9 oz. Since your specified value of 15.5 lies in between these limits, the process appears to be O.K.! (You don't have enough data to call a shut-down as yet!)

Checking Pharmaceutical Specifications

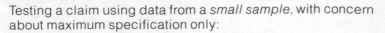

Testing a claim using data from a *small sample*, with concern about maximum specification only:

In this example let's say you're called in to help out the buyer for a large chain of drugstores. A large shipment of *Dr. Sam's Cough Medicine and Elixir of Life* has just arrived. The manufacturer claims that the preparation contains 8% alcohol. The buyer needs to be certain that the population's mean alcohol content is no greater than 8%. He can only get data on a small sample: 5 bottles were selected at random and analyzed. The bottles showed 7.85%, 8.33%, 7.97%, 8.31% and 7.76% alcohol upon test. Should you advise the buyer to reject the shipment? He tells you he'd like to be 95% sure of his decision.

Target: In this case you need to find out all you can about the population mean (μ) from the small sample. Your primary concern is that the mean alcohol content of the shipment is not over 8% before accepting it.

Tools: In this case you're dealing with a small sample (n < 30), so you should use the statistical analysis method suitable for small sample analysis as outlined below.
First, using your calculator, enter the sample data with the [Σ+] key, and calculate the sample mean ($\bar{x}$) and sample standard deviation (s_x) with the [2nd] [Mean] and [2nd] [S.Dev.] key sequences. Next, using the formula below, calculate the predicted range for the population mean:

Predicted range for the population mean $= \bar{x} \pm \dfrac{s_x}{\sqrt{n}} t$

In this formula
$\bar{x}$ is the sample mean,
s_x the sample standard deviation
n the number of items in the sample (5)
t the "t" value you find in the Appendix.
In this case the t value is found in *Table B,* because you are concerned with only one limit. In this table, locate the t value for the degree of certainty you require (here 95%) and the number of degrees of freedom, (df) equal to n − 1= 4.(You should find a t value of 2.132.)

If you can be 95% sure that the alcoholic content of the "Elixir" is greater than 8%, you plan to reject the shipment.

Keying It In: First, enter your data using the $\boxed{\Sigma+}$ key, and calculate the sample mean and standard deviation values:

Press	Display/Comments
$\boxed{2nd}$ $\boxed{CA}$	**0** Clear the entire machine
$\boxed{2nd}$ $\boxed{Fix}$ 2	**0.00** Set display to 2 decimal places
7.85 $\boxed{\Sigma+}$	**1.00** Enter your data: the
8.33 $\boxed{\Sigma+}$	**2.00** calculator keeps count
7.97 $\boxed{\Sigma+}$	**3.00** of the number of entered
8.31 $\boxed{\Sigma+}$	**4.00** data points
7.76 $\boxed{\Sigma+}$	**5.00**
$\boxed{2nd}$ $\boxed{Mean}$	**8.04** the sample mean $(\bar{x})$.
$\boxed{2nd}$ $\boxed{S.Dev.}$	**0.26** the sample standard deviation (s_x).

Now clear the calculator and calculate the predicted range of the population mean. First calculate $\dfrac{s_x}{\sqrt{n}}t$ and store it, then calculate $\bar{x} \pm \dfrac{s_x}{\sqrt{n}}t$.

$\boxed{2nd}$ $\boxed{CA}$	**0** Clears everything
$\boxed{2nd}$ $\boxed{Fix}$ 2	**0.00** Set decimal to 2
0.26 $\boxed{\div}$ 5 $\boxed{\sqrt{x}}$ $\boxed{\times}$ 2.132	
$\boxed{=}$ $\boxed{STO}$ 1	**0.25**
	Now add $\bar{x}$ to calculate $\bar{x} + \dfrac{s_x}{\sqrt{n}}t$
$\boxed{+}$ 8.04 $\boxed{=}$	**8.29** upper limit
	Now calculate $\bar{x} - \dfrac{s_x}{\sqrt{n}}t$
8.04 $\boxed{-}$ $\boxed{RCL}$ 1 $\boxed{=}$	**7.79** lower limit

Decision Time:

8% Dr. Sam's claimed value

7.79%   8.29%

Predicted range of the population mean
based on your small sample.

Based on this analysis you'd accept the shipment. As far as you
can tell, based on the small number of samples you've tested, the
actual amount of alcohol may be as low as 7.79%. Since Dr. Sam's
claimed value is 8% — you have no argument with the shipment.
In this case the entire predicted range of the population mean
would have to be greater than 8% before you'd reject the shipment
with 95% certainty.

Checking Claims on Defective Parts

Checking on a proportion of defective parts — with concern about maximum percentage defective only:

In this "case history" you are called in to aid the manufacturer of *Elflasho* flashlights. He's just received his first shipment of flashlight bulbs from a new manufacturer — and wants to be particularly sure he's got a good shipment before accepting it. Testing the parts is quite simple in this case — they either light or they don't — so a sizeable sample can be easily tested. The new bulb manufacturer, *Brite Spot Systems, Inc.* insists that the shipment (population) will contain no more than 12% defective bulbs.

The *Elflasho* line foreman has 250 of the bulbs tested, and of these, 43 fail (17.2%). He asks your advice — should he accept or reject the shipment based on this data? He'd like to be 90% sure the lot has more than 12% defective bulbs, before he rejects the shipment and looks for a new vendor.

Target: In this case you're dealing with a claim about a *proportion,* and so you should use a statistical technique especially suited to handling the problem.

First, you use the formula below to calculate the *predicted range of the population mean,* as in previous examples. In this case, however, instead of the population mean being a numerical value (such as weight, or % volume) it's the *proportion of defective parts in the population.*

The formula for the range in this case is:

Predicted Range of the Population Mean Proportion $= \overline{P} \pm \left(\dfrac{\overline{P}(1 - \overline{P})}{n}\right)^{1/2} z.$

where: P is the proportion of defective parts found in the sample

(In this case $\dfrac{43}{250}$ or 0.172)

n is the sample size (250)
and
z is the z value found from *Table A* in the *Appendix.*

You're concerned with one limit here (you should reject if the shipment is over 12% defective, and accept otherwise). Since you wish to be 90% sure of the reject decision, the z value from *Table A* is found from column 1 to be 1.28.

Once you've calculated a range for the population mean, you'll compare it to the manufacturer's claim — and make your decision.

Keying It In: You already know that the proportion of defective parts in the sample is 17.2% or 0.172. Now evaluate the expressions

$$\overline{P} + \left(\frac{\overline{P}(1 - \overline{P})}{n}\right)^{1/2}z \text{ and } \overline{P} - \left(\frac{\overline{P}(1 - \overline{P})}{n}\right)^{1/2}z$$

to calculate the predicted range of the mean.

Begin by evaluating $\left(\frac{\overline{P}(1 - \overline{P})}{n}\right)^{1/2}z$, and storing it.

By looking ahead, you can see this problem needs to be solved twice. Storing the first key sequence in program memory allows you to change variables, such as z (degree of certainty), and repeat problem solution with just a few keystrokes.

First, key the problem into program memory assuming P is stored in memory 0, n in memory 1 and z in memory 2.

Press

2nd CA

2nd Lrn
RCL 0 × (1 − RCL 0)
÷ RCL 1 = √x ×
RCL 2 = STO 3
+ RCL 0 = 2nd R/S

RCL 0 − RCL 3 = 2nd R/S

Display/Comments

0 Clears entire machine. Use 2nd Rst when clear all is not desirable.

00 00 Calculator in learn mode
09 00 First R/S stops
15 00 program to display
20 00 upper limit and second
25 00 R/S displays lower limit.

0 Since the last R/S is at location 31, the calculator automatically leaves the learn mode.

Now enter the known values into data memories and run the program.

Press

.172 STO 0
250 STO 1
1.28 STO 2
2nd Rst 2nd Fix 3

2nd R/S
2nd R/S

Display/Comments

0.172 Store P in memory 0.
250. Store N in memory 1.
1.28 Store z in memory 2.
1.280 Reset program to step 00 and display to 3 places.

0.203 Upper limit
0.141 Lower limit

NOTE: Do not clear or turn off calculator.

Decision Time:

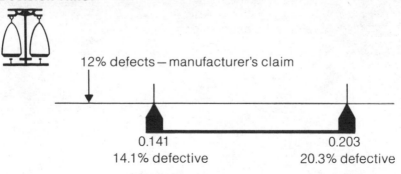

12% defects — manufacturer's claim

0.141
14.1% defective

0.203
20.3% defective

Predicted range for the mean percentage
of defective parts in the population

In this case your sample is telling you that the lowest expected
percentage of defective parts is 14.1%. You're 90% sure that the
manufacturer is *not* living up to his claim and *Elflasho's* needs.
Based on this analysis, you advise their foreman to reject
the shipment.

Going Further: As it turns out, the foreman at *Elflasho* is not
immediately ready to ship back the bulbs. (It seems the president

of *Brite Spot Systems* is also the son-in-law of
Mr. Elflasho.) He needs to be *very* sure. You can re-check
the decision at a higher degree of certainty quite easily.
Let's say you both agree that if he's 95% sure the
shipment is bad — it will go back — and hang the consequences.
First locate the z score in table A for a 95% degree of certainty.
Store the new value for z in memory 2 and rerun the program.

Press	Display/Comments
1.65 [STO] 2	**1.650** Store new z in memory 2.
[2nd] [Rst]	**1.650** Reset program to step 00.
[2nd] [R/S]	**0.211** Upper limit
[2nd] [R/S]	**0.133** Lower limit.

Answer: at 95% certainty — you'd *still* reject the shipment!

Testing for Change

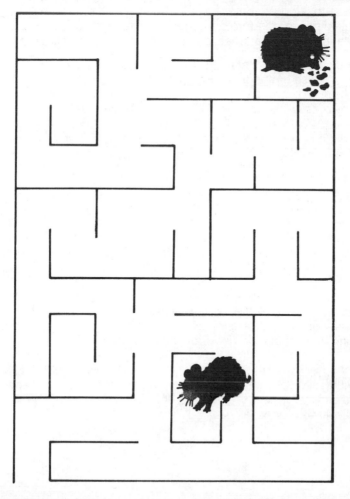

Introduction

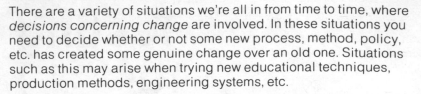

There are a variety of situations we're all in from time to time, where *decisions concerning change* are involved. In these situations you need to decide whether or not some new process, method, policy, etc. has created some genuine change over an old one. Situations such as this may arise when trying new educational techniques, production methods, engineering systems, etc.

In some situations a change may appear overwhelming, and it's an "open and shut" case that something is clearly different. In some other cases, however, it may appear that some improvement has been made—but it's not an overwhelming change. Here's where decision-making becomes more difficult. A decision to endorse or institute a new procedure or process in such a situation, based on data from small samples, can be a pretty tricky business.

Several methods from statistics are available to aid in the study of change. These methods involve some fairly sophisticated techniques—but as before we'll try to boil the *use* of them down to a series of step-by-step procedures. Your advanced professional calculator—with AOS and parentheses helping out—will be a powerful ally here. (In fact, *without* your calculator handling the arithmetic involved, using these techniques would be quite a hassle.)

The specific statistical method we'll be focusing on in this chapter may be called a confidence interval procedure. This procedure often works together with another one called the "F-test". These two procedures enable you to decide—with a degree of certainty that *you* select—whether or not a genuine difference exists between one set of data and another (assuming that the populations are, at least, approximately normal). In cases where your decision involves a considerable sum of money—these tests can be an important part of your decision-making process. In cases where lives may be involved—such as in pharmaceutical research or immunology—these procedures can be crucial!

This chapter uses "confidence interval" and "F-test" methods in analyzing two "case histories" where a decision must be made based on whether or not a change or difference exists between the results of two processes.

Coated vs. Bare Pipe

Uncorrected "confidence interval" method for analyzing change:

Let's consider a case where you're "called in" to help out with a decision on an oil pipeline. A new pipe supplier on the scene (Apex) claims that a new "neverust" coating process on his company's product will provide "up to three times longer life" over standard, noncoated pipe. The decision to change to the new pipe will involve a significant unit cost increase, and your pipeline requires several hundred miles of pipe — so you need to be pretty sure (let's say 95%) about any decision made.

You ask to see the *data* which supports Apex's claim of up to three times longer life. As it turns out, all of the data that Apex has are the results of six experiments. In each experiment a length of standard pipe and a length of coated pipe were buried side by side (in six different locations), and the weight loss due to corrosion was measured (in ounces per foot per year). The results of their tests are tabulated below:

APEX NEVERUST PIPE CO.
TEST DATA
(yearly weight loss in ounces/foot/year)

Uncoated Steel Pipe	Apex Neverust Coated Pipe
3.68	2.68
1.28	0.45
1.84	0.92
3.68	1.69
1.83	0.05
6.00	0.16

The agent claims that from this data you can "clearly see" that Apex's new coating process results in pipe that lasts "up to three times longer". He has nothing more to say on the matter — so you tell him you'd like to think about it.

Target: Your goal in this case is to determine just how much you know about the pipe's performance, based on only the sample. Since the sample (6 coated & 6 uncoated pipes) is small, methods of "statistical inference" will be important here. What you really

 need to do is to predict what the mean difference in yearly weight loss would be between a coated and an uncoated pipeline, based on the experimental data from Apex (the sample) at a 95% degree of certainty.

Tools: First, you can take a "statistical look" at the sample data by examining the mean and standard deviation values for the pipe weight loss.

Then, using the methods of statistical inference, you can determine the range of difference in weight loss between pipelines built of coated and uncoated pipe. There are two procedures to follow in making this prediction:

■ The first is called an "F-test" — this is sort of a "pre-testing" process that lets you know whether or not the second technique — the "confidence interval" — needs any adjustments.

■ After the "F-test" is "passed" you then use the "confidence interval" procedure to make your prediction. (Procedures to follow if the "F-test" is *not* passed are examined in the next example.)

You'll notice that the "F-test" and "confidence interval" procedures examined here involve mathematical manipulations that will put your advanced professional calculator "through its paces". We'll take it one step at a time.

Keying It In: First, take a statistical look at the Apex Company's sample data, using your calculator to find the mean weight loss, standard deviation, and the square of the standard deviation (used in the tests later) for both coated and uncoated pipe data:

Uncoated Pipe:

Press			**Display/Comments**
2nd	CA		**0** Clear all
2nd	Fix	4	**0.0000** Fix decimal at 4 places
3.68	Σ+		**1.0000** Enter data for
1.28	Σ+		**2.0000** uncoated pipe
1.84	Σ+		**3.0000**
3.68	Σ+		**4.0000**
1.83	Σ+		**5.0000**
6.00	Σ+		**6.0000**
2nd	Mean		**3.0517** Mean weight loss for uncoated pipe
2nd	S.Dev.		**1.7653**
x^2			**3.1163**

Coated Pipe:

Press	**Display/Comments**
2nd CA	**0** Clear all
2nd Fix 4	**0.0000** Fix decimal at 4 places
2.68 Σ+	**1.0000** Enter data for
0.45 Σ+	**2.0000** coated pipe
0.92 Σ+	**3.0000**
1.69 Σ+	**4.0000**
0.05 Σ+	**5.0000**
0.16 Σ+	**6.0000**
2nd Mean	**0.9917** Mean weight loss for coated pipe
2nd S.Dev.	**1.0213**
x^2	**1.0430**

Note: Based on the samples, the mean weight loss for the standard pipe is 3.0517 and the mean weight loss for the Neverust pipe is 0.9917. From these results (without using statistical inference) it appears that the Apex claim of about three times less weight loss for Neverust pipe is justified. But how much can you "depend" on this result?

Now, for purposes of the "F-test" we will need to identify the data with the greatest standard deviation as the "high" data, and the data with the lowest value standard deviation as the "low" data. We'll use the subscripts "H" for high and "L" for low to tell these apart — and, in this case, the uncoated pipe data has the greatest standard deviation and will be called the "high" data. Let's tabulate what we have at this point, along with all the necessary labels, below. (The F test here is said to be a "one tailed" test — we're testing to see if Sx_H^2 is greater than Sx_L^2.)

Yearly Weight Loss Data (oz/ft/year)	*Uncoated Pipe*	*Coated Pipe*
Sample mean	$3.0517 = \bar{x}_H$	$0.9917 = \bar{x}_L$
Standard deviation	$1.7653 = Sx_H$	$1.0213 = Sx_L$
square of standard deviation	$3.1163 = Sx_H^2$	$1.0430 = Sx_L^2$
number of samples	$6 = n_H$	$6 = n_L$

Now, to conduct the "F-test" you calculate the value of $\dfrac{Sx_H^2}{Sx_L^2}$, and compare this to an "F value" found in *Table D* in the *Appendix*. The F value you look for in the table should be for $n_H - 1$ degrees of freedom (in this case $6 - 1$ or 5) for the numerator, and $n_L - 1$ degrees of freedom (in this case $6 - 1$ or 5) for the denominator; and a 95% degree of certainty. (The F value you will find in this case is $F = 5.05$) If this F value is *greater* than your calculated value for $\dfrac{Sx_H^2}{Sx_L^2}$, the F-test is "passed" and you can proceed to the prediction using "confidence interval" procedures. So, to calculate $\dfrac{Sx_H^2}{Sx_L^2}$:

Press

| 2nd | CA |
| 2nd | Fix | 4
| 3.1163 | ÷ | 1.0430 | = |

Display/Comments

0

0.0000

2.9878 calculated value of $\dfrac{Sx_H^2}{Sx_L^2}$

So, in this case, since the F value of 5.05 is greater than your calculated value for $\dfrac{Sx_H^2}{Sx_L^2}$ of 2.9878, the F test is "passed".

Now you can go on and use the "confidence interval" procedure to determine the range of difference in mean weight loss between the coated and uncoated pipe.

To find the range, look in *Table C* in the *Appendix* and find the t value for the degree of surety you want (here 95%), and for $n_H + n_L - 2$ degrees of freedom (in this case, $6 + 6 - 2$ or 10). (The t value you will find is 2.228) Now you can calculate the *range of predicted difference* for the means, using the fairly complex-looking formula below:

Range of difference between means

$$= (\bar{x}_H - \bar{x}_L) \pm \left[\left(\frac{((n_H - 1)Sx_H^2 + (n_L - 1)Sx_L^2)}{(n_H + n_L - 2)} \right) \left(\frac{1}{n_H} + \frac{1}{n_L} \right) \right]^{1/2} t$$

In our case:

$\bar{x}_H = 3.0517$ $n_H = 6$ $Sx_H^2 = 3.1163$ $t = 2.228$
$\bar{x}_L = 0.9917$ $n_L = 6$ $Sx_L^2 = 1.0430$

Press

| 2nd | CA |
| 2nd | Fix | 4
| 3.0517 | − | 0.9917 | = |
| STO | 1 |

Display/Comments

0 Clear entire machine

0.0000 Set display to 4 decimal places

2.0600 Calculate & store

2.0600 $(\bar{x}_H - \bar{x}_L)$

Now calculate the remainder of the formula (AOS is a big help
here — just carefully key it in):

Keys	Result
((	
((6 [−] 1)	
[×] 3.1163 [+]	**15.5815**
(6 [−] 1) [×]	
1.0430) [÷]	**20.7965** Value of the numerator
(6 [+] 6 [−] 2)	**10.0000** Value of denominator
) [×]	**2.0797**
(6 [1/x] [+] 6 [1/x])	**0.3333**
)	**0.6932**
[√x̄]	**0.8326**
[×] 2.228 [=] [STO] 2	**1.8550** Value of right hand expression in formula

Now to complete calculation,
first add this to $(\bar{x}_H - \bar{x}_L)$

| [+] [RCL] 1 [=] | **3.9150** |

Next, subtract second term
from $(\bar{x}_H - \bar{x}_L)$

| [RCL] 1 [−] [RCL] 2 [=] | **0.2050** |

Decision Time: So, based on this analysis you can be 95% sure,
based on Apex's data, that the *difference in the means* between a

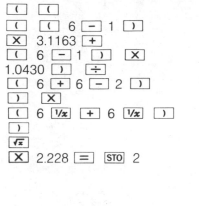

coated and an uncoated pipeline will be between 3.9150
and 0.2050 ounces per foot per year. What this means is
that you are 95% certain that the coated pipe process
will perform better than the uncoated pipe by as much
as 3.9150 ounces per foot per year *or* by as little as 0.2050 ounces
per foot per year (or any value in between). This is all you can tell
based on only six experiments. Apex's claim of "up to" three times
better performance seems to be technically O.K. — but they left out
the "other side" of the claim which could read: "or as little as a few
percent better performance". At any rate all you really have to base
your decision on is a predicted range for the *difference between
the means*.

With this information it's now time to closely scrutinize what extra
costs are involved in changing to the coated pipe, how long the
pipeline needs to last, and the other factors surrounding the
decision. Your analysis of this data should put you in a better
bargaining position with Apex — and also lets you see clearly just
how much (or how little) information can be drawn from a small
series of experiments.

Biological Data Analysis

Corrected "confidence interval" method for analyzing change:

In this case a young biology student approaches you for help in analyzing data he's just taken from an experiment. He is testing to see whether or not a certain drug has any effect on the intelligence level of hamsters — as measured by the time it takes the hamsters to complete a simple "maze" test. Nine hamsters were fed the drug and given the test, while a "control" group of 13, which were *not* treated, were given the same test. The student has already tabulated the data for the two groups of hamsters:

	No Drug	Treated with Drug
number of hamsters in sample	13	9
mean time to complete maze	110.02	101.58
standard deviation	9.9116	2.8566
square of standard deviation	98.24	8.16

The student's instructor looked at the data and told the student that it appeared to him that there was no "significant difference" between the two groups. The student, however, feels very sure that the drug *did* create a change. He asks you to determine if he can go back to his instructor and state that he's 99% sure that the drug really did improve the hamsters' performance on the test.

Target: In this case you're trying to determine all you can about the performance of the drug based on a small series of tests. What statistical inference enables you to do is to calculate, at a certainty level you select, a confidence interval (range) of difference in intelligence of hamsters treated with the drug and those not treated with the drug. The method used to calculate this range is a *two part* process. First, an "F-test" is used on the data, then based on the results of this test you calculate either a "corrected" or an "uncorrected" confidence interval.

Tools: To perform the F test we need to identify the data with the greatest standard deviation as the "high" data, and data with the lowest value standard deviation as the "low" data. We'll be using the subscripts "H" and "L" to tell these two groups apart. In this case, we'll tabulate the data we have, with all of the necessary labels, below:

	No Drug	Treated with Drug
number of hamsters	$13 = n_H$	$9 = n_L$
mean time on maze test (sec)	$110.02 - \bar{x}_H$	$101.58 = \bar{x}_L$
standard deviation	$9.9116 = Sx_H$	$2.8566 = Sx_L$
square of standard deviation	$98.24 = Sx_H{}^2$	$8.16 = Sx_L{}^2$

First, to conduct the F test, calculate the value of $\frac{Sx_H^2}{Sx_L^2}$, and compare this to the appropriate F value found in *Table E* in the *Appendix*. (The appropriate F value in this case is $n_H - 1$ or 12 degrees of freedom for the numerator, $n_L - 1$ or 8 degrees of freedom for the denominator, and a 99% degree of certainty.) At a 99% degree of certainty, $F = 5.67$. If your calculated value is less than the value from the table, the F test is "passed" and you can proceed right on to calculating the confidence interval. If, however, your calculated value is greater than the F value you found from the table, a *corrected* "confidence interval" procedure must be used. The F test here is said to be a "one tailed" test, testing to see if Sx_H^2 is greater than Sx_L^2.

Keying It In: Begin by calculating $\frac{Sx_H^2}{Sx_L^2}$.

Press	Display/Comments
[2nd] [CA]	**0** Clear entire machine
[2nd] [Fix] 3	**0.000** Fix display at 3 decimal places
98.24 [÷] 8.16 [=]	**12.039** Value of $\frac{Sx_H^2}{Sx_L^2}$

Since this value is *greater* than the value found from the F table for this problem (5.67), the F test is *not* passed, so a corrected "confidence interval" procedure will be used for the rest of the problem. The object of this calculation is to arrive at a *range for the differences* in performance between hamsters treated with the drug and those not treated with the drug.

The correction to the "confidence interval" procedure essentially boils down to arriving at a *corrected number of degrees of freedom* for the problem. Once this corrected number of degrees of freedom is calculated, then the appropriate t value is used in a formula to calculate the predicted range of difference in the population means.

The corrected number of degrees of freedom is given by the formula:

$$\text{corrected degrees of freedom} = \frac{1}{\left[\dfrac{K^2}{(n_H - 1)} + \dfrac{(1 - K)^2}{(n_L - 1)}\right]}, \quad \text{where } K = \frac{\dfrac{Sx_H^2}{n_H}}{\left(\dfrac{Sx_H^2}{n_H} + \dfrac{Sx_L^2}{n_L}\right)}$$

This is a case where your "advanced professional" machine is a real help in "slicing through" the mathematics. First evaluate K:

Press	**Display/Comments**
2nd CA	**0** Clear entire machine
2nd Fix 3	**0.000** Fix decimal at 3 places
98.24 ÷ 13 =	
STO 1 ÷	**7.557** Value of $\dfrac{Sx_H{}^2}{n_H}$
(RCL 1 + 8.16	
÷ 9)	**8.464** Value of denominator
= STO 2	**0.893** Value of K stored in memory 2

Now calculate the "corrected" number of degrees of freedom:

1 ÷	**1.000**
(RCL 2 x^2 ÷ (	
13 − 1) +	**0.066**
(1 − RCL 2)	
x^2 ÷	**0.011**
(9 − 1)) =	**14.734** is the corrected number of degrees of freedom

Now, to continue with the analysis, this value of the number of degrees of freedom is used to look up a t value from *Table C* in the *Appendix* (at a 99% degree of certainty). This t value is used to calculate the range using the formula:

Range of difference between means

$$= (\bar{x}_H - \bar{x}_L) \pm \left[\left(\frac{((n_H - 1)Sx_H{}^2 + (n_L - 1)Sx_L{}^2)}{(n_H + n_L - 2)} \right) \left(\frac{1}{n_H} + \frac{1}{n_L} \right) \right]^{1/2} t$$

In our case

$\bar{x}_H = 110.02$ $n_H = 13$ $Sx_H{}^2 = 98.24$
$\bar{x}_L = 101.58$ $n_L = 9$ $Sx_L{}^2 = 8.16$

When looking in *Table C* for the approximate value, you'll note that the table only lists t values for integer values of degrees of freedom (14, 15, etc.). Using your calculator you can find the appropriate value of t for 14.734 degrees of freedom using a process called "interpolation".

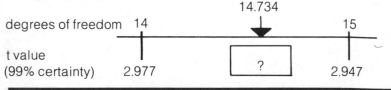

degrees of freedom 14 — 14.734 — 15

t value (99% certainty)   2.977   ?   2.947

Between degrees of freedom 14 and 15 the t values go from 2.977
to 2.947. To find the t value for 14.734 degrees of freedom:
$2.977 - [(14.734 - 14)(2.977 - 2.947)]$

Press	Display/Comments
2nd CA	**0** Clear entire machine
2nd Fix 3	**0.000** Fix decimal at 3 places
2.977 − (	**2.977** value of t at 14
(14.734 − 14) ×	**0.734** "distance" from 14 to 14.734
(2.977 − 2.947)	**0.030** "distance" in t values from 14 to 15
) =	**2.955** t value for 14.734

With this t value you can now calculate the range of difference
between means using the formula given previously:

Press	Display/Comments
2nd CA	**0** Clear entire machine
2nd Fix 3	**0.000** Set decimal places to 3
110.02 − 101.58 =	
STO 1	**8.440** The value of $\bar{x}_H - \bar{x}_L$ stored in memory 1
((	Next calculate the
((13 − 1) ×	**1178.880** righthand term in the equation
98.24 +	
(9 − 1) ×	
8.16) ÷	**1244.160**
(13 + 9 − 2)	
×	**62.208**
(13 1/x + 9 1/x)	**0.188**
)	**11.697**
√x × 2.955 = STO 2	**10.106**
	Now add $(\bar{x}_H + \bar{x}_L)$
+ RCL 1 =	**18.546** Upper limit for difference between means
	Subtract second term from first:
RCL 1 − RCL 2 =	**−1.666** Lower limit for difference between means

Decision Time: Based on the data you have, you can state with 99% surety that the difference between the means lies between 18.546 and −1.666. Now if the drug had no effect on the hamsters' performance, you would expect *no difference* (zero difference) between the means. Since the range of predicted values of the difference between means includes the value zero, you *cannot be sure* (at a 99% degree of certainty) that any real change has taken place when the hamsters are treated with the drug. As the instructor suspected there is no "statistically significant" difference between the two groups at the 99% confidence level. You might suggest that *more data* be taken at this point.

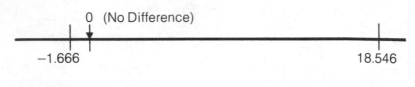

0   (No Difference)

−1.666   18.546

Going Further: Would this analysis predict a significant difference between the two groups at the 95% confidence level?

Answer: Yes

Keys to
Financial
Decisions

Introduction

KEYS TO
FINANCIAL
DECISIONS   5

Healthy money should never lie stagnant, but should be kept in situations where it is "growing" constantly. Sound financial planning should always take this growth into account. There are a variety of business investment and savings situations providing growth for cash. Making plans and predictions in these situations can involve some fairly detailed calculations. Your advanced professional calculator is equipped with several features and functions especially powerful in keeping track of "the value of money".

In this chapter we'll begin with some quite basic cash flow and growth situations, then move on to several more involved examples. Along the way we'll consider personal as well as business decisions involving investments — including a lease or buy decision situation. The formulas and principles involved are not difficult to understand, but the mathematics involved could be really tiresome without your calculator. With your calculator saving time and adding accuracy, planning is easier and faster — and you're free to "try out" many different alternatives without a huge "investment" in time and labor.

Compound Interest

(THE BASIC PLAN FOR
LETTING YOUR MONEY GROW)

One straightforward way to obtain a certain amount of cash growth
is to deposit your money in an interest-bearing account. Money in
most savings accounts grows according to the "compound
interest" formula — which is a basic tool that's important in many
financial planning and decision-making situations. We'll consider
a simple example and "build up" this formula.

Let's say you deposit $958 in a savings account which pays 0.6%
interest each month. You know you'll be able to leave the money in
the account for only three complete months — then you'll need to
withdraw most of it for a business purchase. What is the value of the
money after three complete months?

Target: You need to find the value of your deposit ($958)
left in a compound interest account for three months, at
an interest rate of .6% per month. Along the way we'll
develop a formula for calculating compound interest.

Your reasoning might go something like this: At the end of the first
month your money had earned $958 \times (0.6\%)$ in interest. So, the total
cash accumulated in your account at the end of the first month was
$958 + 958(0.6\%)$. We can rewrite this as $958 \times (1 + 0.6\%)$ — that is,
the amount of cash you have at the *end* of the first month is
$(1 + 0.6\%)$ times the amount you had at the beginning of the month.

In the same way the amount of money you have at the end of *any*
month is just $(1 + 0.6\%)$ times the amount at the beginning of that
month. The amount at the end of the second month is

$$\left[958 \times (1 + 0.6\%) \right] \times (1 + 0.6\%), \text{ which can be written as}$$

$958 \times (1 + 0.6\%)^2$. Continuing in this manner, the amount of money
you now have at the end of three months can then be expressed as:
$958 \times (1 + 0.6\%)^3$. This formula is easy to evaluate on your
calculator. In addition, the programmable feature allows you to
store the calculation sequence in program memory. And by storing
the needed data values in memories, you can easily change the
amount deposited, the interest rate or the number of periods and
repeat the problem as often as you want to.

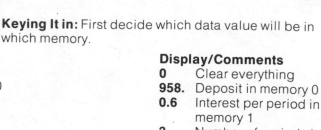

Keying It in: First decide which data value will be in which memory.

Press		**Display/Comments**	
2nd CA		**0**	Clear everything
958 STO 0		**958.**	Deposit in memory 0
.6 STO 1		**0.6**	Interest per period in memory 1
3 STO 2		**3.**	Number of periods in memory 2

Now, with the values in memories 0, 1, and 2, key the problem keystrokes into program memory.

2nd Lrn		**00 00** Enter learn mode.
RCL 0 ✕ (1 +		**06 00** Key in problem as
RCL 1 %) yˣ		**11 00** written, substituting
RCL 2 =		**14 00** memory recalls for actual values.
2nd R/S 2nd Rst		**16 00**
2nd Lrn		**0** Exit learn mode.

Since the values are already stored in memories, to solve the problem, simply run the program.

2nd Rst		**0.** Resets program to step 00.
2nd Fix 2		**0.00** Set for two decimal display.
2nd R/S		**975.35** The value of $958 at the end of 3 months.

To find the value after 4 months, just store 4 in memory 2 and run the program.

4 STO 2		**4.00**
2nd R/S		**981.20** The value of $958 at the end of 4 months.

Going Further: When you are considering more complex problems involving compound interest or payments, a diagram called a *time line* will often help clarify the situation. A time line for this problem would look like this:

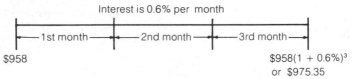

Interest is 0.6% per month

—1st month—— ——2nd month—— ——3rd month—

$958 $958(1 + 0.6%)³
                                                    or $975.35

The "value" of your money is shown for the beginning and end of the three months. On time line diagrams there is a notation commonly used to label various points in your problem situation. The amount of money you're starting with now ($958) is called the *present value* (PV) of your money. The value at the end of the three months is called the *future value* (FV) of your money. The 0.6% interest per month may be labeled i% interest per time interval. The number of time intervals you're considering is usually labeled n, and is marked as shown on the line.

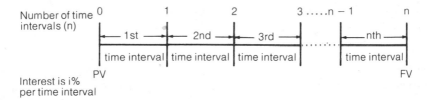

Number of time intervals (n)

Interest is i% per time interval

Using these symbols we can now write the "compound interest" formula for calculating future value of money:

$$PV \times (1 + i\%)^n = FV$$

All this formula says is: To calculate the future value (FV) of your money n time intervals from now (at i% interest per interval), just take the present value and multiply it by $(1 + i\%)^n$. There's nothing to it on your calculator.

Here's an important point to keep in mind when using this formula: The interest rate (i%) must be for the *same time interval* used on the time line. We'll be stressing this point as we go along, but keep it in mind—forgetting it is a common source of error in handling these problems.

In many business or everyday life situations you're setting aside a certain amount of cash today for an anticipated *future* purchase or expense. In situations such as this you use the compound interest formula in the "reverse direction". Consider this example:

You're planning to buy a new car in two years for $5000. Your bank has an account available paying 0.8% per month interest. How much money would you have to deposit *now* to have the $5000 ready then?

 Target: In this case you need to find the *present value* (PV) of a specified future value amount (FV). The time period you're considering is 2 years (24 months) at 0.8% interest per month.

Tools: In analyzing this example you may find a time line helpful:

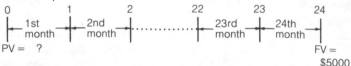

The basic formula for compound interest we worked up in the previous section is $PV \times (1 + i\%)^n = FV$. In this case you need to calculate a present value, so solve this equation for PV:

$$PV = \frac{FV}{(1 + i\%)^n} \quad \text{or}$$
$$PV = FV \times (1 + i\%)^{-n}$$

This formula just states that if you need to calculate the present value of some future amount, just multiply by $(1 + i\%)^{-n}$.
In our example: $\quad PV = 5000 \times (1 + 0.8\%)^{-24}$

Press	Display/Comments
[2nd] [CA]	**0** Clear all.
[2nd] [Fix] 2	**0.00** Fix decimal at 2 places
5000 [X] [(] 1 [+] .8 [%] [)]	
[yˣ] 24 [+/−] [=]	**4129.69** = PV

You need to deposit $4,129.69 to have $5000 in two years. Notice the similiarity of this problem to the previous problem. In fact, you can store FV in memory 0, i in memory 1 and n in memory 2, then by adding [+/−] before [=] in the previous program, you can solve for PV with any FV, i, or n value you choose.

Payroll Deductions
FUTURE VALUE OF PAYMENTS

Most often in personal or business saving, you're putting away a small amount at regular intervals — building up an account. For handling future value of payments the compound interest formula is just used repeatedly — and as you'll see in this example, a general formula for calculating future value in a regular payment situation can be easily worked up.

Let's say that you've started depositing $75 on the 15th of each month (through payroll deduction) in your company's credit union. You can't get in contact with the credit union right now, but you need to know how much cash you will have accumulated in 6 months, one year, and in 5 years. The credit union pays 0.5% per month — starting the 1st of the month following the payment.

 Target: In this case you want to find the future value that accumulates when you make a series of regular payments for a specified number of payment intervals.

Tools: A time line will be helpful in visualizing this example, and we'll work with the compound interest formula:
$$FV = PV(1 + i\%)^n \text{ or } PV = FV(1 + i\%)^{-n}$$
As we go through the solution we'll arrive at a general formula for handling this situation which is easily evaluated on your calculator.

The time line for the 6 payment situation is shown here:

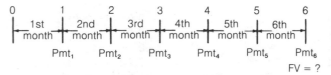

One way to approach the problem is to just calculate the future value of each of the payments at the end of the 6 months using the compound interest formula, and then add up all the results. (Often when calculating the future value of an amount of money, it's said that you "move" the money into the future. You may see this term used in discussions on future value.)

So, at the end of the 6th month Pmt_6 will not have earned any interest, Pmt_5 will have earned interest for one month, Pmt_4 will have earned for two months, and so on.

The total amount of cash you've accumulated at the end of the 6th month is then:
$$Pmt_6 + Pmt_5(1 + i\%) + Pmt_4(1 + i\%)^2 + Pmt_3(1 + i\%)^3 + Pmt_2(1 + i\%)^4 + Pmt_1(1 + i\%)^5.$$

PAYROLL DEDUCTIONS
(FUTURE VALUE
OF PAYMENTS)

KEYS TO
FINANCIAL
DECISIONS

5

The programmable feature of the calculator can really be put to work to save you keystrokes in solving this problem. Notice that Pmt $(1 + i\%)$ is common for each payment term. Pmt_6 still has $(1 + i\%)$; however, since it hasn't had time to gain interest $Pmt_6 \times (i + i\%)^0 = Pmt_6 \times 1$, or simply Pmt_6. Since the payments are equal, the only difference between terms in our equation is the number of periods, n, which increments from 0 to 5. The following key sequence shows how to key in only one payment term and let the calculator do the repetitive work. The value for n is in memory 0 and you simply add 1 to memory 0 for each subsequent calculation. The subsequent calculations are summed together by leaving a ⌈+⌉ pending at the end of each calculation.

Press

| 2nd | CA | 2nd | Lrn |

75 ⌈X⌉ ⌈(⌉ 1 ⌈+⌉ .5 ⌈%⌉ ⌈)⌉
⌈yˣ⌉ RCL 0 ⌈X⌉ 1 SUM 0 ⌈+⌉

| 2nd | R/S | 2nd | Rst |

| 2nd | Lrn |

Display/Comments

00 00 Clear all and enter learn mode.

10 00 Key in payment term,
18 00 sum 1 to memory 0 and leave + pending.

20 00 Stop to show result, get ready to reset.

0 Exit learn mode.

Now run the program as follows:

| 2nd | Rst |

| 2nd | Fix | 2
2nd	R/S
2nd	R/S
2nd	R/S
2nd	R/S	2nd	R/S	2nd	R/S

0. Resets program to step 00.
0.00 Fix decimal at 2 places.
75.00 One month
150.38 Two months
226.13 Three months
455.66 Six months

You will have $455.66 at the end of six months. You can continue for as many months as you wish. To start over, just press CLR STO 0 then 2nd R/S again.

Going Further: There's an easier way — a real time saver for problems like this. A series such as the one we've just worked with
$$1 + (1 + i\%) + (1 + i\%)^2 + (1 + i\%)^3 + (1 + i\%)^4 + (1 + i\%)^5$$
is called a geometric series of 6 terms. The sum of a series like this can be simplified to $\dfrac{((1 + i\%)^6 - 1)}{i\%}$

So the amount you have at the end of the 6 months can be written as: $75 \times \left(\dfrac{((1 + 0.5\%)^6 - 1)}{0.5\%}\right)$

PAYROLL DEDUCTIONS
(FUTURE VALUE
OF PAYMENTS)

KEYS TO
FINANCIAL
DECISIONS

5

Now you need to key the new problem into program memory.
Notice that this problem does not require summation of successive
calculations, and again the value n is assumed to be stored in
memory 0 to make it convenient to repeat the calculation for a
different number of periods.

Press

`2nd` `CA` `2nd` `Lrn`

Display/Comments

00 00 Clear all and center
learn mode.

75 `X` `(` `(` `(` 1 `+` .5
`%` `)`
`yˣ` `RCL` 0 `−` 1 `)` `÷` .5 `%`
`)` `=` `2nd` `R/S` `2nd` `Rst`
`2nd` `Lrn`

12 00 Key in formula as written.

22 00
26 00
0 Exit learn mode.

Now run the program.

`2nd` `Rst` `2nd` `Fix` 2
6 `STO` 0 `2nd` `R/S`

0.00 Reset and fix decimal.
455.66 Amount after six
months.

Notice that this is the same result found before by the "long" method.
Do not clear all or turn off calculator.

Now in general, the future value (FV) will be:

$$FV = Pmt \times \left(\frac{((1 + i\%)^n - 1)}{i\%} \right)$$

Using this general formula it's now easy to compute the amount
you will have in your savings account at the end of one year:

$$\text{Value at } 12 \text{ months} = 75 \times \left(\frac{((1 + 0.5\%)^{12} - 1)}{0.5\%} \right)$$

Press

12 `STO` 0 `2nd` `R/S`

Display/Comments

925.17 at the end of one year

The amount you will have at the end of 5 years is:

$$\text{Value at } 60 \text{ months} = 75 \times \left(\frac{((1 + 0.5\%)^{60} - 1)}{0.5\%} \right)$$

Press

60 `STO` 0 `2nd` `R/S`

Display/Comments

5232.75 at the end of 5 years

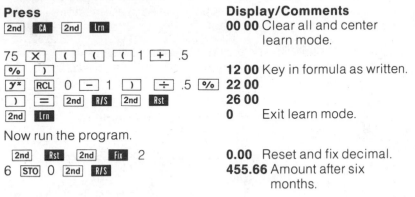

Decision Time: Using this formula and your calculator
it's now easy to predict and check out "what if" for any
set of payroll deductions at various interest rates. Such
calculations enable you to quite easily and accurately
examine various investment and savings alternatives.

You're Rich – But...

(PRESENT VALUE OF A
SERIES OF PAYMENTS)

Your Uncle Clyde liked you pretty well, but he didn't have much faith
in your money handling ability. That's probably why he left your
brother the farm and you with a series of payments. The will said
that you were to receive $1000 per year for the next 8 years (in one
lump sum at the end of the year). An urgent business "opportunity"
has arisen – and you'd like to have as much cash as possible
right now.

Making a quick call to the bank you find that they'll gladly buy the
series of payments from you at their present value – figured at 8%
annual interest. Your problem – is this a wise decision?

Target: You need to find the present value of the
payments (how much the money is worth now).

Tools: A time line will help you visualize the situation, and we'll also
work with the formula to calculate the present value of some
future amount:

$$PV = FV \, (1 + i\%)^{-n}$$

As we go through the solution we'll arrive at a general formula for
handling this situation which is easily evaluated on your calculator.

The Time Line:

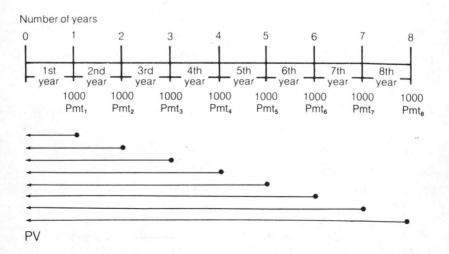

YOU'RE RICH, BUT...
(PRESENT VALUE OF A
SERIES OF PAYMENTS)

KEYS TO
FINANCIAL
DECISIONS

5

One way to approach the problem is to just calculate the present value of each of the payments and then add up all of the results.

$$PV = Pmt_1 (1 + i\%)^{-1} + Pmt_2 (1 + i\%)^{-2} + Pmt_3 (1 + i\%)^{-3}$$
$$+ Pmt_4 (1 + i\%)^{-4} + Pmt_5 (1 + i\%)^{-5} + Pmt_6 (1 + i\%)^{-6}$$
$$+ Pmt_7 (1 + i\%)^{-7} + Pmt_8 (1 + i\%)^{-8}$$

Now since all of the payments are equal you "factor them out" to get

$$PV = Pmt [(1 + i\%)^{-1} + (1 + i\%)^{-2} + \dots (1 + i\%)^{-8}]$$

There's an easier way. The series:

$$(1 + i\%)^{-1} + (1 + i\%)^{-2} + \dots (1 + i\%)^{-8}$$

is another geometric series of 8 terms. The sum of a series like this can be simplified to

$$\left(\frac{1 - (1 + i\%)^{-8}}{i\%} \right)$$

Now, in general, for any series of payments of equal amounts at the *end* of n equal time intervals, the present value will be:

$$PV = Pmt \frac{(1 - (1 + i\%)^{-n})}{i\%}$$

Now let's find the present value of the $1000 a year payments.
In our case,

$$PV = 1000 \times \left(\frac{(1 - (1 + 8\%)^{-8})}{8\%} \right)$$

Keying It In:

Press	Display/Comments
[2nd] [CA]	**0** Clear all
[2nd] [Fix] 2	**0.00** Set decimal to 2 places
1000 [×] [(] [(]	**1000.00** The amount of yearly payment
1 [−] [(] 1 [+] 8 [%] [)]	**1.08** The (1 + 8%) term
[yˣ] 8 [+/−] [)] [÷]	
8 [%] [)] [=]	**5746.64** PV

YOU'RE RICH, BUT...
(PRESENT VALUE OF A
SERIES OF PAYMENTS)

KEYS TO
FINANCIAL
DECISIONS

5

Decision Time: Now's the time to closely examine your "business opportunity". Decide what the prospects of success are very carefully — before deciding to accept $5746.64 of ready cash.

Going Further: You were dissatisfied with the present value of the payments so you had your uncle's lawyer recheck the will. He found the provisions read that you may receive the payments at the *first* of the year. You'd like to compare the present value of the payments if they are made at the first of the year with the present value of the payments made at the end of the year. One way to approach the problem is to calculate the present value of each of the payments, using the present value formula:

$$PV = FV (1 + i\%)^{-n}$$

The present value of the payment is: $Pmt_1 + Pmt_2 (1 + i\%)^{-1} + Pmt_3 (1 + i\%)^{-2} + Pmt_4 (1 + i\%)^{-3} + Pmt_5 (1 + i\%)^{-4} + Pmt_6 (1 + i\%)^{-5} + Pmt_7 (1 + i\%)^{-6} + Pmt_8 (1 + i\%)^{-7}$

Notice Pmt_1 is already in present value. Since all the payments are equal, you can "factor them out" to get:

$$Pmt \times [1 + (1 + i\%)^{-1} + (1 + i\%)^{-2} + ... (1 + i\%)^{-7}]$$

Again, there's an easier way. The series:

$1 + (1 + i\%)^{-1} + (1 + i\%)^{-2} + ... (1 + i\%)^{-7}$ is another geometric series. The sum of a series like this can be simplified to:

$$\left(1 + \frac{(1 - (1 + i\%)^{-(7)})}{i\%}\right)$$

Now, in general, for any series of payments of equal amounts at the *beginning* of n equal time intervals (in advance) earning interest of i% per time interval, the present value will be:

$$PV = Pmt \left(1 + \frac{(1 - (1 + i\%)^{-(n-1)})}{i\%}\right)$$

YOU'RE RICH, BUT...
(PRESENT VALUE OF A
SERIES OF PAYMENTS)

KEYS TO
FINANCIAL
DECISIONS

5

Now let's find the present value of the $1000 a year payments made at the beginning of each year for 8 years at 8% annual interest.

$$PV = 1000 \times \left(1 + \frac{(1 - (1 + 8\%)^{-(8-1)})}{8\%}\right)$$

Press	**Display/Comments**
2nd CA	**0** Clear all
2nd Fix 2	**0.00** Set decimal at 2 places
1000 ✕ (	
1 + (1 −	
(1 + 8 %)	
yˣ 7 +/−) ÷	
8 % =	**6206.37** The present value of the payments if they're made at the beginning of each year.

Let's find how much more the present value of the payments is if payments are made "in advance" (at the beginning of each period) or "in arrears" (at the end of each period).

− 5746.64 =   **459.73**

Decision Time: Now you may want to re-evaluate your decision based upon the increase in present value due to receiving the payments in advance.

Business has been going pretty well for you lately and the word is getting around. In fact, your brother-in-law has asked you for a loan. He wants to borrow $4535 to improve his home. He's willing to pay you 6% annual interest, and claims he'll pay the loan off in 3 equal yearly payments starting next year. You decide to help him out, and need to calculate just how much the loan payments should be.

Target: You need to determine the amount of the loan payments for your brother-in-law. Along the way we'll work up a general formula for calculating loan payments.

Tools: We'll be using a time line to help visualize the problem, along with the formula for present value of a series of payments received at the *end* of each payment period. (When payments are received at the *end* of the periods you're considering, they're said to be received "in arrears". Payments received at the beginning of the period are said to be received "in advance".)

$$PV = Pmt \left(\frac{(1 - (1 + i)^{-n})}{i} \right)$$

The Time Line:

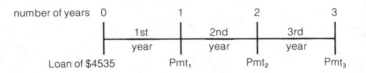

YOU'RE THE BANKER
(CALCULATING LOAN
PAYMENTS)

KEYS TO
FINANCIAL
DECISIONS

5

The present value of the payments from your brother-in-law for
3 years at 6% is $4535 and using the above formula you can write:

$$4535 = \text{Pmt} \times \left(\frac{(1 - (1 + 6\%)^{-3})}{6\%} \right)$$

Solving for the Pmt gives

$$\text{Pmt} = \frac{4535}{\left(\dfrac{(1 - (1 + 6\%)^{-3})}{6\%} \right)}$$

Keying It In:

Press

2nd CA
2nd Fix 2
4535 ÷ ((
1 − (1 + 6 %
) y^x 3 +/−)
÷ 6 %) =

Display/Comments

0 Clear all
0.00 Fix decimal at 2 places

1696.59 Pmt

Decision Time: The annual payments should be
$1696.59. Do you think your brother-in-law will come up
with the money?

Mow Your Own Lawn?

(BUY EQUIPMENT OR
CONTRACT FOR SERVICE?)

The old lawnmower "bit the dust", and you ask yourself if you should buy a new lawnmower at all. You don't particularly like mowing the lawn, trimming the hedge, pulling weeds, etc.... but it will cost $200 per year to have someone contract to take care of the yard.

The price of a new lawnmower is $329.95, and if you were to buy it you would expect to pay about $8 per year for operating and maintenance expenses. The mower would probably last about 6 years, and then you would get rid of it (donate it to a garage sale to help raise money for the school band or some such cause). Keeping in mind that your cash would grow at about 7% per year if you kept it in the bank, you're wondering if you really wouldn't be better off just having the yard done.

Target: You want to take a sound, "cold" look at the situation. What's the *real* difference in cost between paying to have the job done, and buying a new lawnmower to do it yourself?

Tools: A time line will again be used to help in picturing what's going on. We'll also be using the formula for the present value of a series of payments "in arrears":

$$PV = Pmt \left(\frac{(1 - (1 + i\%)^{-n})}{i\%} \right)$$

and also the formula for the present value of a series of payments in advance:

$$PV = Pmt \left(1 + \frac{(1 - (1 + i\%)^{-(n-1)})}{i\%} \right)$$

The time line:

Number of years	0	1	2	3	4	5	6
		1st year	2nd year	3rd year	4th year	5th year	6th year
Cost of Mower	$329.95						
Operating & Maintenance Cost	PV_8	8	8	8	8	8	8
Have someone do the yard	PV_{200}	200	200	200	200	200	

MOW YOUR OWN LAWN?
(BUY EQUIPMENT OR
CONTRACT FOR SERVICE?)

KEYS TO
FINANCIAL
DECISIONS

5

One way to approach this problem is to consider the fact that if you didn't buy the mower the \$329.95 cost and \$8/year operating cost could be earning 7% annual interest. So you would find the present value of these amounts (labeled $PV_{329.95}$ and PV_8 on the time line).

$$PV_{329.95} = 329.95$$

$$PV_8 = 8 \times \left(\frac{(1 - (1 + 7\%)^{-6})}{7\%} \right)$$

Now you want to compare this to the cost of having the lawn done (PV_{200}). In situations like this, use the formula for the present value of a series of payments in advance:

$$PV_{200} = 200 \times \left(1 + \frac{(1 - (1 + 7\%)^{-(6-1)})}{7\%} \right)$$

Keying It In:

Note the similarity of the two problems. Keystrokes can be saved by entering the "similar part" of the calculation into program memory. Memory 0 is used to store n or n−1 values.

Press	Display/Comments
2nd CA 2nd Lrn	**00 00** Clear all and enter learn mode.
(1 − (1 + 7 %)	**09 00**
y^x RCL 0 +/−) ÷ 7 %	**17 00** Partial equation $\dfrac{(1 - (1 + 7\%)^{-(n)}}{7\%}$
= 2nd R/S 2nd Rst	**20 00**
2nd Lrn	**0** Exit learn mode.

Now solve for PV_8

6 STO 0 2nd Fix 2	**6.00** Store n in memory 0.
2nd Rst 8 × (2nd R/S	**38.13** $= PV_8$
+ 329.95 =	**368.08** This is the present value of the mower and the maintenance payments.

Now compare this to the present value of the cost of having the lawn done:

5 STO 0	**5.00** Store n−1 in memory 0.
200 × (1 + 2nd R/S	**1020.04** $= PV_{200}$
− 368.08 =	**651.96** The difference

MOW YOUR OWN LAWN?
(BUY EQUIPMENT OR
CONTRACT FOR SERVICE?)

KEYS TO
FINANCIAL
DECISIONS

5

Decision Time: The difference in cost between buying the mower and mowing it yourself and paying someone else to mow it is $651.96. The decision—can you afford it?

Going Further: While your calculator is still turned on, maybe you would like to know how much you can pay yourself at the first of each year to mow your own lawn.

0		1		2		3		4		5		6
	1st year		2nd year		3rd year		4th year		5th year		6th year	

P   P   P   P   P   P

651.96

To find how much each of these payments will be, use the formula for the present value of a series of payments in advance:

$$651.96 = \text{Pmt} \left(1 + \frac{(1 - (1 + 7\%)^{-(6-1)})}{7\%} \right)$$

Solving for the Pmt gives:

$$\text{Pmt} = \frac{651.96}{\left(1 + \frac{(1 - (1 + 7\%)^{-(6-1)})}{7\%} \right)}$$

Keying It In:

Press	Display/Comments
	651.96 Previous result
$\div$ $($ 1 $+$ 2nd R/S	**127.83**

You can pay yourself $127.83 each year to keep your own lawn. At this point you can look at your decision in a new light. Is it worth it?

Buy a Rented House? (INVESTMENT DECISION)

You're considering buying a house that is presently rented for $375 per month as an investment. You have $10,000 available cash for the investment. You realize that buying a house involves some risk, so you are planning the move only if you can make a sizeable profit on the deal (15% annual rate).

After checking with a realtor, you find that you can buy the house by placing $10,000 down and assuming a $25,000 mortgage. You figure that your expenses, including mortgage payments, will be about $250 per month. You expect to keep the property for 10 years, sell the property, pay off the mortgage, and net $20,000. Should you invest in the house?

Target: Analyze the situation and see if you can achieve your overall goal of 15% effective annual interest on your investment.

A Note on Interest: You can calculate equivalent interest rates with different compounding intervals by using the compound interest formula. For example, suppose you deposit amount (A) for a year at 15% per year interest.

|←——————— one year ———————→|
A   A (1 + 15%)

(You would have A (1 + 15%) at the end of the year.) Now say you would like to know what monthly interest rate (i%) is equivalent to 15% per year. To determine the equivalent monthly rate, assume you deposit the same amount (A) in an account which pays i% per month.

|←———— 12 months ————→|
A   A (1 + i%)^{12}

The interest rates will be equivalent if the final amounts are equal.

$$A (1 + 15\%) = A (1 + i\%)^{12}$$

Now the equation may be solved for i%.

Dividing both sides by A gives:

$$(1 + 15\%) = (1 + i\%)^{12}$$

taking the 12th root, $\sqrt[12]{(1 + 15\%)} = (1 + i\%)$

subtracting 1 from both sides,

$$\sqrt[12]{(1 + 6\%)} - 1 = i\%$$

On your calculator [2nd] [CA] [(] 1 [+] 15 [%] [)] [$^x\sqrt{y}$] 12 [−] 1 [=] 0.0117149 or about 1.17% per month interest.

Tools: The basic tools in analyzing these situations are a time line diagram, and the compound interest formula:

$$PV = FV (1 + i\%)^{-n}$$

as well as the formula for the present value of a series of payments in advance:

$$PV = Pmt \left(1 + \frac{(1 - (1 + i\%)^{-(n-1)})}{i\%}\right)$$

The Time Line: The interest is 1.17% per month (and 10 years is 120 months).

Number of months	0	1	2	119	120
	1st month	2nd month		120th month	

Your Investment 10,000

You will be receiving $375 each month for rent, and spending $250 each month for the mortgage payment and maintenance. You can consider that the net result is actually a series of monthly payments of $125 in your favor, and consider them on the same time line:

125   125   125   125   0

(1)

Also, at the end of the 10 years you will receive $20,000 cash from the sale of the house.

(2)   20,000

One way to arrive at a conclusion on this investment is to compare your $10,000 investment to the $125 payments plus the $20,000 selling price (assuming that you make the 1.17% monthly interest desired). If the present value of the net rent payments plus the present value of the selling price exceed your $10,000 investment amount—the investment is a sound one.

Step ① Find the present value of the $125 monthly income. Note that the payments are made at the beginning of each month; therefore use the formula for the present value of a series of payments in advance.

$$PV = 125 \times \left(1 + \frac{(1 - (1 + 1.17\%)^{-(120-1)})}{1.17\%}\right)$$

Step ② Find the present value of the $20,000 you expect to make when you sell the house:

$$20,000 \times (1 + 1.17\%)^{-120}$$

Now add the results from step ① and step ② to get the present value of the income from the investment.

Keying It In:

Press	Display/Comments
[2nd] [CA]	**0** Clear all
[2nd] [Fix] 2	**0.00** Set display at 2 decimal places
	Calculate Step ①
125 [×] [(] 1 [+]	
[(] 1 [−] [(] 1 [+]	
1.17 [%] [)] [yˣ]	
119 [+/−] [)]	
[÷] 1.17 [%] [)] [=]	**8132.27** The present value of the payments if you make 1.17% monthly.
	Calculate Step ②
20000 [×] [(] 1 [+]	
1.17 [%] [)] [yˣ] 120	
[+/−] [=]	**4952.45** The present value of the 20,000 selling profit. Now add the two present values together.
[+] 8132.27 [=]	**13084.72**

 Decision Time: Based on this analysis, the investment is a good move. The income from the house will actually be creating revenues for you that are equivalent to a 1.17% per month return or 15% per year on an initial investment of $13,084.72. Since you can "purchase" these profits for only $10,000, the house is indeed a sound investment.

Lease It Up...
(LEASE OR BUY DECISION)

Your business is considering buying or leasing a new computer. According to the financial lease agreement, the company would pay $36,000 per year for 5 years. The company could buy the machine outright (including a 5 year service contract) for $135,000. You have determined that no resale value on the machine can be expected after 5 years. If the computer is installed, it is expected to save the company $46,000 per year. Your company expects a yearly return of 15% on all funds of this sort invested. The company is a healthy one, with good credit, and can borrow at 8% annual interest from local banks.

 Target: In this case you want to analyze the situation in two parts:
Decision 1: Is it cheaper to lease or buy the computer, based on the data you have and the company's financial situation? Once you've made that decision, then you want to go on to

Decision 2: Is it a sound investment for the company to acquire the computer at all, based on the 15% yearly return the company requires on investments?

Tools: Again a time line diagram will be used to get a picture of the situation, and the cash values you'll need to make your decisions will be calculated using the formula for the present value of a series of payments "in arrears" (received at the end of the period):

$$PV = Pmt \left(\frac{(1 - (1 + i\%)^{-n})}{i\%} \right)$$

and the present value of a series of payments in advance formula:

$$PV = Pmt \left(1 + \frac{(1 - (1 + i\%)^{-(n-1)})}{i\%} \right)$$

Decision 1: Should you lease or buy the computer? The loan rate is 8%.

Find the present value of the payments if the computer is leased, which is also called the Equivalent Purchase Price (EPP) of the lease.

$$EPP = 36000 \left(1 + \frac{(1 - (1 + 8\%)^{-(5-1)})}{8\%} \right)$$

Keying It In:

Press

2nd CA
2nd Fix 2
36000 × (
1 + (1 −
(1 + 8 %)
y^x 4 +/−)
÷ 8 %
) =

Display/Comments

0 Clear all
0.00 Set decimal at 2 places

155236.57 The Equivalent
Purchase Price of the lease

Decision Time: If the money is borrowed at 8%, the
Equivalent Purchase Price of the lease is $155,236.57.
Comparing this to the purchase price of $135,000,
purchasing the computer is the better alternative.

Decision 2: Should you acquire the computer at all? The critical
question is: Is the present value of the savings the computer
generates — assuming a 15% return — enough to justify the $135,000
investment?

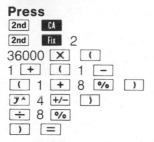

	0	1	2	3	4	5
		1st year	2nd year	3rd year	4th year	5th year
Investment 135,000						
compared to						
Payments	PV_2	46,000	46,000	46,000	46,000	46,000

Find the present value of the $46,000 yearly savings, PV_s.

$$PV_s = 46000 \times \left(\frac{(1 - (1 + 15\%)^{-5})}{15\%} \right)$$

Then, compare the present value of the savings to the $135,000 investment.

Keying It In:

Press

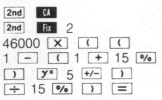

| 2nd | CA |
| 2nd | Fix | 2 |

46000 ⊠ ⦅ ⦅
1 ⊟ ⦅ 1 ⊞ 15 %
⦆ y^x 5 +/− ⦆
÷ 15 % ⦆ =

Display/Comments

0 Clear all
0.00 Set decimal at 2 places

154199.13 The present value of the savings

Decision Time: Acquiring the computer is a good move! The savings it creates amount to an equivalent of a 15% return on an investment of $154,199.13. You are achieving this level of return with an actual investment of only $135,000 — so the investment would be a sound one — based on this analysis.

A Little Theory...

"The mathematical order of the universe is our answer to the pyramids of chaos. On every side of us we see bits of life that are completely beyond our understanding — we label them unusual, but we really don't want to acknowledge them. The only thing that really exists is statistics. The intelligent person is the statistical person."

from *The Investigation* by Stanislaw Lem copyright © 1974 by the Seabury Press, Inc. Used by permission.

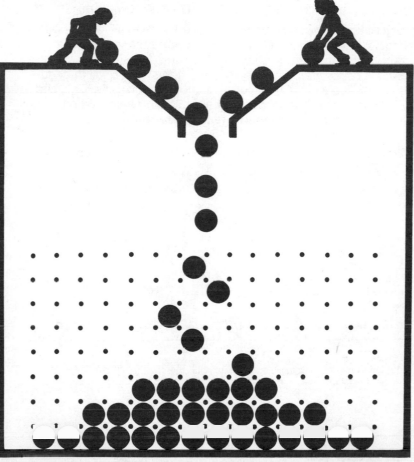

Introduction

As mentioned in the introduction to this book, our primary concentration is on the "how to use" side of statistical tools that are especially applicable in a variety of business and everyday life situations. We hope you find these techniques valuable (and even enjoyable) to use in bringing more accuracy into your decision making with your calculator. But—there are always those folks who ask: Why and how does this stuff work, anyway?

The full answer to all parts of that question probably would involve an extended statistics course—and some sources for further reading are suggested in the *Bibliography*. For those of you who'd like to brave a quick survey of the key elements of what we've been using—here we go:

Start with a Simple Example (Small Population)

To get into the theory let's start with an analysis of a small body of data—one we can completely handle. Suppose you are examining test scores for 5 people on a simple exam (statisticians would say that this *population* consisted of *5 elements*). Let's say that (out of a perfect score of 10) the scores for the 5 pupils are 4,5,6,7, and 8. With your calculator you can immediately and easily calculate the *population mean* (labeled μ) and the *population standard deviation* (labeled σ):

Press	Display/Comments
[2nd] CA	**0** Clear entire machine
[2nd] Fix 2	**0.00** Set display to readout 2 decimal places
4 [Σ+]	**1.00**
5 [Σ+]	**2.00** Calculator keeps a count
6 [Σ+]	**3.00** of your data entries.
7 [Σ+]	**4.00**
8 [Σ+]	**5.00**

Now—to find the population mean (μ):

[2nd] Mean	**6.00**

To find the *population standard deviation* (σ) you use the special key sequence:

[2nd] Var [√x]	**1.41**

(We'll be saying more about why you use *this* sequence to find σ a little later.)

So with this *small population* you can easily and directly analyze all the data in straightforward fashion as illustrated below:

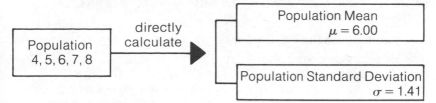

What About a Huge Population?

Now here's the rub — what happens when you'd like to know what the population mean (μ) really is, but the population is made up of thousands (or even millions) of items? Even with your calculator helping, entering all that data may be nearly impossible. In addition, sometimes the measurement you're taking may *destroy* the item. For example — imagine that you're testing a shipment (population) of 5000 batteries to check on their lifetime. You have to deplete a battery to know how long it lasted in the lifetime test. If you did this to the entire population — you'd know *exactly* what the mean lifetime for the population was. You'd also have no batteries left to use!

In situations like this, one logical alternative is to select a smaller number of items from the population — a *sample* — and test them. This is where the science of statistics comes in. Based on analyzing the *smaller* sample — which is cheaper, easier (and more possible) than testing the population — you can use *methods of statistical inference* to make statements about the population mean (μ). Your first step would be to calculate the sample mean ($\bar{x}$) and the sample standard deviation (s_x). Then you'd apply some statistical techniques to get back to information about the population, as diagrammed below:

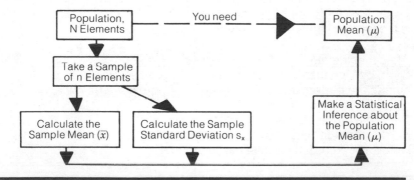

Now—the "roundabout" path by which you use your sample data to get back to information about the population contains *some* chance. It's fairly logical that the *larger* your sample *is*, the less chancy your statements about the mean are.

The Sample and the Population

Now we focus on one key point in the situation. When you take a small sample out of the large population—how "representative" is it? In our battery example if you just happened to pick a lot of "duds", you could wind up underrating an entire shipment based on their performance. Likewise, if by chance you only picked real "winners"—you may overrate the shipment. In this discussion we'll be focusing on what the chances are that the sample mean ($\bar{x}$) is near the population mean (μ).

To give you a feel for how statisticians study this situation—we'll go back to our small *population* of 5 test scores (one we can handle) and consider the situation when *samples* of 2 test scores are taken from it and examined. (In practice a population this small would not be handled using statistics—but by using it to examine the processes statisticians use—we'll demonstrate some important concepts.) Now concentrate on this process:

As we've already discussed, our five test scores were 4, 5, 6, 7, 8. The population mean (μ) was 6. What would happen if you picked out 2 of these scores at random (a sample)—and checked *their* mean ($\bar{x}$)? What would your chances be that the *sample mean* would also be 6— equal to the population mean?

To answer this timely and interesting question you first need to focus on *all the possible samples of two test scores* you can draw out of our population of 5, and then examine the sample means for each possibility. This is the way statisticians first began looking at the problem of statistical inference. We'll tabulate all of the possible samples of 2 test scores, along with their means, in the table on the following page.

(Note that the method of selection for the test scores at random could be visualized as: putting each score on a slip of paper— putting the papers into a hat, shaking well, picking one out and noting it— *replacing it in the hat*— shaking again—picking again. The replacement factor is important. When samples are taken without replacement from a population of N elements, a "correction factor" is entered into statistical inferences.)

Population of 5 Test Scores: *4, 5, 6, 7, 8*

In this table we are tabulating all possible ways of picking a sample of 2 elements; as well as the mean of each sample.

All Possible Samples of 2 Elements	Value of the Mean for Each Sample	Label for Mean Value
4, 4	4.0	$\bar{x}_1$
4, 5	4.5	$\bar{x}_2$
4, 6	5.0	$\bar{x}_3$
4, 7	5.5	$\bar{x}_4$
4, 8	6.0	$\bar{x}_5$
5, 4	4.5	$\bar{x}_6$
5, 5	5.0	$\bar{x}_7$
5, 6	5.5	$\bar{x}_8$
5, 7	6.0	$\bar{x}_9$
5, 8	6.5	$\bar{x}_{10}$
6, 4	5.0	$\bar{x}_{11}$
6, 5	5.5	$\bar{x}_{12}$
6, 6	6.0	$\bar{x}_{13}$
6, 7	6.5	$\bar{x}_{14}$
6, 8	7.0	$\bar{x}_{15}$
7, 4	5.5	$\bar{x}_{16}$
7, 5	6.0	$\bar{x}_{17}$
7, 6	6.5	$\bar{x}_{18}$
7, 7	7.0	$\bar{x}_{19}$
7, 8	7.5	$\bar{x}_{20}$
8, 4	6.0	$\bar{x}_{21}$
8, 5	6.5	$\bar{x}_{22}$
8, 6	7.0	$\bar{x}_{23}$
8, 7	7.5	$\bar{x}_{24}$
8, 8	8.0	$\bar{x}_{25}$

Now, in a "real life" situation you'd be picking out a sample, measuring *its* mean value ($\bar{x}$), and from that result, trying to calculate or deduce the population mean value (μ). So, *focus your attention on the sample mean values.* This is the data that's available to you – you're actually picking out sample mean values, $\bar{x}$'s, and need to know what your chances are that $\bar{x}$ comes close to the actual value of the population mean (μ). (Remember that your population mean here is 6 – glance at the table and get a "feel" for your chances of picking an $\bar{x}$ of 6 at random.)

What Are Your Chances?

Let's get a picture of how the sample means (the $\bar{x}$'s) vary. We can do this in a simple picture that puts each mean value in its place as shown below:

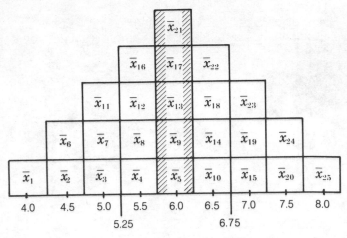

Values for the Sample Means

In this picture we've just put each mean label inside a little "box", and stacked up the boxes according to the value of their means. This picture gives you a feel for what your chances would be of picking a sample at random, and finding one with a sample mean equal to the population mean value of 6. Five of the sample means $\bar{x}_{21}$, $\bar{x}_{17}$, $\bar{x}_{13}$, $\bar{x}_9$ and $\bar{x}_5$ (in the center boxes) each have mean values of 6. In fact, the most probable choice would be a 6 value. It turns out that for large populations (N over 100) and large samples (n over 30), this is a general rule:

The most probable value of $\bar{x}$ is the population mean (μ).

Relative Areas

If you examine the *relative areas* of the boxes you can get a visual picture of the chances that if you pick a sample at random — its $\bar{x}$ will be a 6. There are 25 boxes in all, 5 of them contain 6's, so your chances actually can be visualized as the ratio of the shaded boxes to the total area of all the boxes; or $\frac{5}{25}$ or 20%.

In this picture you can also consider the values of $\bar{x}$ that are *close* to μ. What would your chances be of picking a sample at random whose $\bar{x}$ was 6 ± 0.75? (An $\bar{x}$ value from 5.25 to 6.75?) Again — just count all the boxes containing $\bar{x}$'s between 5.25 and 6.75; and divide by the total number of boxes. Your chances in this case would be $\frac{13}{25}$ or 52%.

Now — let's move from our simple little population and consider for a moment what would happen to our picture if the number of elements in the population increased from 5 to 100, and the sample size were increased from 2 to 30. If we were able to take all the sample means and arrange them pictorially as we did before — we'd see something like the behavior below:

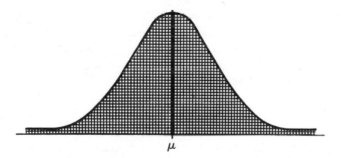

μ

As the boxes get smaller and smaller (they'd be very small in this case, for N = 100 and n = 30 there are 10^{60} boxes) — the outside of our picture smooths out into a classic, symmetric, very important shape — called the *Normal Curve*. As a general rule of thumb, it's assumed in most common situations that the $\bar{x}$'s are *distributed normally* (follow the normal curve) whenever the population has over 100 elements and the sample size is greater than 30.

The Normal Curve

Much has been written about the normal (or "Bell" or "Gaussian")
curve — but we'll be focusing on the *areas under the curve*, and
how we can use the curve to get more information about the
population mean from the sample mean. We'll now be introducing
the role of another key "player" — the *standard deviation of the
sample means*, which is labeled $s_{\overline{x}}$.

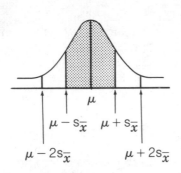

It turns out that because of the fact
that the sample means follow
this "normal" behavior (for large
populations and samples) some
mathematical predictions can be
made using the normal curve that
apply to just about any situation where
large populations and samples are
concerned. We'll present some of
these useful *results* here. Remember
that statisticians calculated these
results by examining areas under
the normal curve.

First of all, examine the normal curve above and note that we've
partitioned its area into 4 sections, each of which is separated by
$s_{\overline{x}}$. Look at the shaded area — it includes all the sample means
whose values are between $\mu - s_{\overline{x}}$ and $\mu + s_{\overline{x}}$. It turns out that ratio
of this area to the total is always the same — 68.26%. This means
that whenever you pick a sample from a population, your chances
are 68.26 out of 100 that you have picked a sample mean that's
within $\pm s_{\overline{x}}$ of the population mean. Another way of saying this is
that you can be 68.26% sure that the *population* mean lies
somewhere in the range of *your sample mean* plus or minus $s_{\overline{x}}$.

Now it turns out that $s_{\overline{x}}$, the *standard deviation of the sample means*,
is fairly easy to calculate from your sample data. For samples with
larger than 30 elements (n > 30), $s_{\overline{x}}$ can be considered equal to

$\dfrac{s_x}{\sqrt{n}}$, where s_x is just the *sample standard deviation*. The sample

standard deviation is readily available — this is the number you see
displayed in your calculator after you enter your sample data (with
the ⟨Σ+⟩ key), and then press ⟨2nd⟩ ⟨S.Dev.⟩

Recapping — Getting to the Predicted Range for μ

So now with the help of the normal curve you can analyze a population, based on a sample, in the following way:

First find the sample mean ($\bar{x}$) and sample standard deviation (s_x), by entering the sample data into your calculator with the $\boxed{\Sigma+}$ key, and then using the $\boxed{2nd}$ $\boxed{\text{Mean}}$ and $\boxed{2nd}$ $\boxed{\text{S.Dev.}}$ key sequences.

Then, using your sample data you can say with 68.26% certainty that the population mean (μ) lies between $\bar{x} + \dfrac{s_x}{\sqrt{n}}$ and $\bar{x} - \dfrac{s_x}{\sqrt{n}}$

That is, you can use your sample data to set up a *predicted range for the population mean*. This range is as close as you can get to the population mean — because of the uncertainty in the process of using *sample* data to draw conclusions about the *population*. You can only state, to a certain degree of certainty, that the population mean lies somewhere in that range.

Analyzing with Large Samples: z Scores

Notice that the predicted *range* for the population mean above, gave us the limits for the value of μ to one specific degree of certainty: 68.26%. In most applications it's advisable for *you to be able to select the degree of certainty* that you desire (or *need*) when making any decision about a population, based on sample data.

To make this easy to do, tables have been constructed based on the areas under different portions of the normal curve. These tables are called tables of "z values" or "z scores", and they enable you to calculate a predicted range for μ to a degree of certainty you select. (A "z value" table is included for your use in the Appendix.)

To use the table — just decide *how sure you want to be* that your calculated range will include the population mean. Check in the z table to find the appropriate z score.

Upper/Lower Limits:

Note that two columns are included in the z table. The column you use to find your z score depends on your particular decision situation — as you'll see in the examples in various chapters in this book. If your decision involves *just* an upper or lower value for μ — just one "limit" — use column I, otherwise, use column II.

To explain why the z values are different for these two situations, consider the normal curve that we have been discussing.

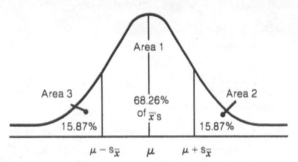

Your chance of picking an $\bar{x}$ in area 1 (range $\mu \pm s_{\bar{x}}$) is 68.26% as discussed earlier. Looking at this another way, your chance of picking an $\bar{x}$ outside of area 1 is $\dfrac{\text{area 2} + \text{area 3}}{\text{total area}}$ or $\dfrac{15.87\% + 15.87\%}{100\%}$

or about $\dfrac{32}{100}$. But suppose you are *only* interested in your chance of picking an $\bar{x}$ greater than $\mu + s_{\bar{x}}$ (checking only an upper limit).

Your chance is $\dfrac{\text{area 2}}{\text{total area}}$ or $\dfrac{15.87\%}{100\%}$ or about $\dfrac{16}{100}$. Since different proportions of the total area are used, different z scores must be used for these two situations — so two columns are provided in the table.

Procedure for Using z Tables to Calculate the Range for μ:

Once you've located the z score, you can calculate the predicted range for μ using the general formula below:

Predicted range for $\mu = \bar{x} \pm \dfrac{s_x}{\sqrt{n}}\, z$

where $\bar{x}$ is your *sample mean*.

s_x is the *sample* standard deviation

Note: For large samples the sample standard deviation (s_x) turns out to be very nearly equal to the *population standard deviation* (usually labeled σ). The formula for the range is always correct when written with σ in place of s_x — and you'll see it written that way quite often in textbooks. z is the "z score" for the degree of certainty you select.

Remember that this particular technique works only for large samples taken from larger populations. (Again the boundary line for large samples is usually taken to be 30 elements, and a large population is considered to be 100 elements or more.)

Analyzing with Small Samples: t Scores

By now the question may have arisen — "What happens when I don't have 30 samples — let's say I've only got 5 or 10? What do I do then?" Statisticians have been busily at work on this problem, too. It turns out that as the number of samples goes below 30, the "normal" curve can no longer be accurately used to describe the distribution of the sample means. Statisticians have found a different family of curves that *does work* — if the population is nearly normally distributed — called t curves.

The shape of any t curve depends on what's called the number of *degrees of freedom* (df) for your particular sample. The number of degrees of freedom in most cases is considered to be equal to the *number of elements in your sample minus one* (df = n − 1). The shapes of various t curves are shown in the figure below. Note for a very large number of degrees of freedom (essentially df = 31 or greater), the t curve *becomes* the normal curve (and z scores can be used).

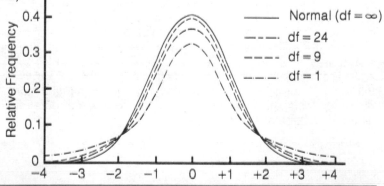

Areas under the t curves have also been tabulated for you in
t "score" tables (*Tables B* and *C* in the *Appendix* are
t score tables for your use). With t scores you can analyze small
sample data in much the same way large sample data is analyzed
with z scores. Here's the step-by-step procedure to follow:

> With the aid of your calculator, calculate the sample mean
> ($\bar{x}$) and sample standard deviation (s_x).

> With this information, you'll be calculating a *predicted* range
> for the population mean. Decide how certain you want (or
> need) to be that the population mean will be in your predicted
> range. For this level of certainty look up the appropriate t
> score in *Table B* or *C* in the *Appendix*. (Use *Table B* if your
> decision involves *only* a maximum or minimum value for μ —
> otherwise use *Table C*.) The value for df you use (the degrees
> of freedom) is the *number of elements in your sample minus
> one* (n − 1).

> Once you've located the t score, the predicted range for the
> population mean can be calculated using the formula:

$$\text{Predicted range for the population mean} = \bar{x} \pm \frac{s_x}{\sqrt{n}} t$$

Summary on Statistical Inference

So basically one process of statistical inference, that can be of
great use to you in decision making, involves taking data from a
sample — and from that calculating a predicted range for the
population mean. This range will tell you, to the degree of certainty
you select, where the population mean lies. In the chapter on
"testing claims" we discuss how you'd compare this predicted
range for the population mean to the mean value claimed by a
manufacturer or supplier for a given product, part, etc. If the *claimed*
mean value *does not* fall in the range you predict — there may be
a problem! As discussed in the examples, you may want to *reject*
a shipment or talk further with your supplier at that point. You'll see
several other examples that involve this application of statistical
inference. Armed with data from a sample, you can make more
accurate decisions about claims being made for a population —
using your calculator and a little statistical math.

The steps involved in the process of statistical inference can be
summarized in the following diagram.

Steps in Analyzing *Sample* Data, to Calculate the *Predicted Range for the Population Mean:*

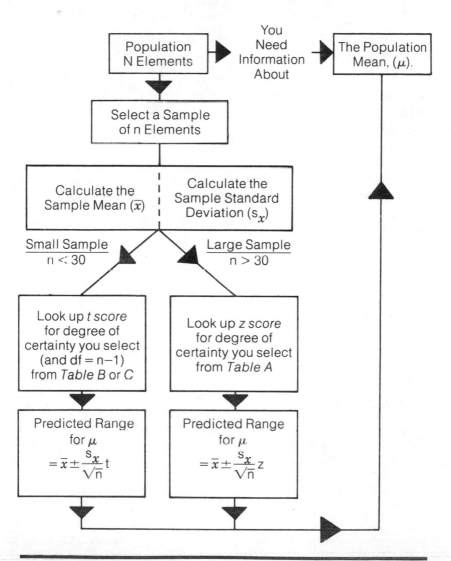

One Further Note on Standard Deviation

Statisticians use two different formulas for calculating standard deviation (in their continued effort to be as accurate as possible). When calculating the *standard deviation of a population* (σ) they use the formula:

$$\sigma = \sqrt{\frac{\Sigma_i(x_i - \overline{x})^2}{N}},$$

where N is the number of elements in the population.

Note: The symbol Σ_i used here (and elsewhere) just means "the sum of". In this case $\Sigma_i(x_i - \overline{x})^2$ means to add all the values of $(x_i - \overline{x})^2$ for i going from 1 to N.

On your calculator, when you're handling an *entire population*, you can enter your data with the [Σ+] key, and calculate:
— the population mean (μ) by pressing [2nd] [Mean]
— the standard deviation of the population (σ) by pressing [2nd] [Var] [√x]

When calculating the *standard deviation of a sample*, (s_x), the formula used is:

$$s_x = \sqrt{\frac{\Sigma_i(x_i - \overline{x})^2}{n - 1}}$$

where n is the number of elements in the sample.

On your calculator, when handling a *sample*, you can enter your data with the [Σ+] key, and calculate:
— the sample mean ($\overline{x}$) by pressing [2nd] [Mean]
— the sample standard deviation (s_x) by pressing [2nd] [S.Dev.]

The complete reasoning behind the difference in these two calculations is beyond the scope of this book. One consideration is that using n − 1 rather than n in the denominator of the sample standard deviation results in a value for s_x that is a *better estimate* for the standard deviation of the population from which the sample is taken. (For values of n > 30, the difference between these two calculations becomes very small.)

Calculator Decision Making

This chapter has surveyed quite a bit of information, quite briefly. In the application chapters of this book we boil down these facts to step-by-step, easy to apply procedures — along with keystroke sequences and sample calculations. *Using* these powerful methods (particularly with your calculator helping out) is really quite easy, and you needn't have studied statistics for years to do it. Once you see the methods "in action" in application situations — many of the procedures we've outlined in this chapter become clearer — and you'll see more clearly how they can help you in calculating better decisions.

We've tried to keep the number of "symbols" used in this book to a minimum — we've introduced and discussed many of them in this chapter — and they're tabulated for you below. (A complete table of all symbols used is also included in a later *Appendix* for your convenience.)

	Population	Sample	Calculator Key Sequence
Number of Elements	N	n	Enter Value of Element, Press $\boxed{\Sigma+}$
Mean	μ	$\bar{x}$	Press $\boxed{\text{2nd}}$ $\boxed{\text{Mean}}$
Standard Deviation	$\sigma = \sqrt{\dfrac{\Sigma_i(x_i - \bar{x})^2}{N}}$	$s_x = \sqrt{\dfrac{\Sigma_i(x_i - \bar{x})^2}{n-1}}$	σ: Press $\boxed{\text{2nd}}$ $\boxed{\text{Var}}$ $\boxed{\sqrt{x}}$ s_x: Press $\boxed{\text{2nd}}$ $\boxed{\text{S.Dev.}}$

$s_{\bar{x}}$ = Standard Deviation
  of the Sample Means

z = z score for a selected
  degree of certainty

t = t score for a selected
  degree of certainty
  and specific number
  of degrees of
  freedom (df)

Appendix

Summary of Symbols

df — degrees of freedom
F — F number from *Table D* or *E*
n — number of elements in a sample
N — number of elements in a population
r — correlation coefficient
r_{test} — test correlation coefficient
Sx_H — standard deviation of the "high" sample
Sx_L — standard deviation of the "low" sample
s_x — standard deviation of a sample
$s_{\bar{x}}$ — standard deviation of sample means
σ — standard deviation of a population
t — t number from *Table B* or *C*
x_i — the ith element of a sample or population
$\bar{x}$ — sample mean
μ — population mean
z — z number from *Table A*

Table A

z Scores*

Degree of Certainty	Column I For Checking <u>Only</u> an Upper or Lower Level	Column II For Checking <u>Both</u> an Upper and Lower Level
60	0.26	0.84
65	0.39	0.94
70	0.53	1.04
75	0.68	1.15
80	0.84	1.28
85	1.04	1.44
90	1.28	1.65
95	1.65	1.96
99	2.33	2.58

* z scores are often called "z values" in this book.

Table B   **t Scores ***
              (For Checking <u>Only</u> an Upper or a Lower Limit)

Degrees of Freedom (df)	◄─────── Level of Certainty ───────►			
	90%	95%	99%	99.5%
1	3.078	6.314	31.821	63.657
2	1.886	2.920	6.965	9.925
3	1.638	2.353	4.541	5.841
4	1.533	2.132	3.747	4.604
5	1.476	2.015	3.365	4.032
6	1.440	1.943	3.143	3.707
7	1.415	1.895	2.998	3.499
8	1.397	1.860	2.896	3.355
9	1.383	1.833	2.821	3.250
10	1.372	1.812	2.764	3.169
11	1.363	1.796	2.718	3.106
12	1.356	1.782	2.681	3.055
13	1.350	1.771	2.650	3.012
14	1.345	1.761	2.624	2.977
15	1.341	1.753	2.602	2.947
16	1.337	1.746	2.583	2.921
17	1.333	1.740	2.567	2.898
18	1.330	1.734	2.552	2.878
19	1.328	1.729	2.539	2.861
20	1.325	1.725	2.528	2.845
21	1.323	1.721	2.518	2.831
22	1.321	1.717	2.508	2.819
23	1.319	1.714	2.500	2.807
24	1.318	1.711	2.492	2.797
25	1.316	1.708	2.485	2.787
26	1.315	1.706	2.479	2.779
27	1.314	1.703	2.473	2.771
28	1.313	1.701	2.467	2.763
29	1.311	1.699	2.462	2.756
30	1.310	1.697	2.457	2.750
40	1.303	1.684	2.423	2.704
60	1.296	1.671	2.390	2.660
120	1.289	1.658	2.358	2.617
∞	1.282	1.645	2.326	2.576

*t scores are often called "t values" in this book.

Table C

t Scores

(For Checking <u>Both</u> Upper and Lower Limits)

Level of Certainty

df	80%	90%	95%	99%	99.9%
1	3.078	6.314	12.706	63.657	636.619
2	1.886	2.920	4.303	9.925	31.598
3	1.638	2.353	3.182	5.841	12.941
4	1.533	2.132	2.776	4.604	8.610
5	1.476	2.015	2.571	4.032	6.859
6	1.440	1.943	2.447	3.707	5.959
7	1.415	1.895	2.365	3.499	5.405
8	1.397	1.860	2.306	3.355	5.041
9	1.383	1.833	2.262	3.250	4.781
10	1.372	1.812	2.228	3.169	4.587
11	1.363	1.796	2.201	3.106	4.437
12	1.356	1.782	2.179	3.055	4.318
13	1.350	1.771	2.160	3.012	4.221
14	1.345	1.761	2.145	2.977	4.140
15	1.341	1.753	2.131	2.947	4.073
16	1.337	1.746	2.120	2.921	4.015
17	1.333	1.740	2.110	2.898	3.965
18	1.330	1.734	2.101	2.878	3.922
19	1.328	1.729	2.093	2.861	3.883
20	1.325	1.725	2.086	2.845	3.850
21	1.323	1.721	2.080	2.831	3.819
22	1.321	1.717	2.074	2.819	3.792
23	1.319	1.714	2.069	2.807	3.767
24	1.318	1.711	2.064	2.797	3.745
25	1.316	1.708	2.060	2.787	3.725
26	1.315	1.706	2.056	2.779	3.707
27	1.314	1.703	2.052	2.771	3.690
28	1.313	1.701	2.048	2.763	3.674
29	1.311	1.699	2.045	2.756	3.659
30	1.310	1.697	2.042	2.750	3.646
40	1.303	1.684	2.021	2.704	3.551
60	1.296	1.671	2.000	2.660	3.460
120	1.289	1.658	1.980	2.617	3.373
∞	1.282	1.645	1.960	2.576	3.291

Degrees of Freedom (df)

Table D

Values of F for 95% Level of Certainty

Degrees of Freedom of the Numerator →

Denom. df	1	2	3	4	5	6	7	8	9	10	12	15	20	30	60	120	∞
1	161.4	199.5	215.7	224.6	230.2	234.0	236.8	238.9	240.5	241.9	243.9	245.9	248.0	250.1	252.2	253.3	254.3
2	18.51	19.00	19.16	19.25	19.30	19.33	19.35	19.37	19.38	19.40	19.41	19.43	19.45	19.46	19.48	19.49	19.50
3	10.13	9.55	9.28	9.12	9.01	8.94	8.89	8.85	8.81	8.79	8.74	8.70	8.66	8.62	8.57	8.55	8.53
4	7.71	6.94	6.59	6.39	6.26	6.16	6.09	6.04	6.00	5.96	5.91	5.86	5.80	5.75	5.69	5.66	5.63
5	6.61	5.79	5.41	5.19	5.05	4.95	4.88	4.82	4.77	4.74	4.68	4.62	4.56	4.50	4.43	4.40	4.36
6	5.99	5.14	4.76	4.53	4.39	4.28	4.21	4.15	4.10	4.06	4.00	3.94	3.87	3.81	3.74	3.70	3.67
7	5.59	4.74	4.35	4.12	3.97	3.87	3.79	3.73	3.68	3.64	3.57	3.51	3.44	3.38	3.30	3.27	3.23
8	5.32	4.46	4.07	3.84	3.69	3.58	3.50	3.44	3.39	3.35	3.28	3.22	3.15	3.08	3.01	2.97	2.93
9	5.12	4.26	3.86	3.63	3.48	3.37	3.29	3.23	3.18	3.14	3.07	3.01	2.94	2.86	2.79	2.75	2.71
10	4.96	4.10	3.71	3.48	3.33	3.22	3.14	3.07	3.02	2.98	2.91	2.85	2.77	2.70	2.62	2.58	2.54
11	4.84	3.98	3.59	3.36	3.20	3.09	3.01	2.95	2.90	2.85	2.79	2.72	2.65	2.57	2.49	2.45	2.40
12	4.75	3.89	3.49	3.26	3.11	3.00	2.91	2.85	2.80	2.75	2.69	2.62	2.54	2.47	2.38	2.34	2.30
13	4.67	3.81	3.41	3.18	3.03	2.92	2.83	2.77	2.71	2.67	2.60	2.53	2.46	2.38	2.30	2.25	2.21
14	4.60	3.74	3.34	3.11	2.96	2.85	2.76	2.70	2.65	2.60	2.53	2.46	2.39	2.31	2.22	2.18	2.13
15	4.54	3.68	3.29	3.06	2.90	2.79	2.71	2.64	2.59	2.54	2.48	2.40	2.33	2.25	2.16	2.11	2.07
16	4.49	3.63	3.24	3.01	2.85	2.74	2.66	2.59	2.54	2.49	2.42	2.35	2.28	2.19	2.11	2.06	2.01
17	4.45	3.59	3.20	2.96	2.81	2.70	2.61	2.55	2.49	2.45	2.38	2.31	2.23	2.15	2.06	2.01	1.96
18	4.41	3.55	3.16	2.93	2.77	2.66	2.58	2.51	2.46	2.41	2.34	2.27	2.19	2.11	2.02	1.97	1.92
19	4.38	3.52	3.13	2.90	2.74	2.63	2.54	2.48	2.42	2.38	2.31	2.23	2.16	2.07	1.98	1.93	1.88
20	4.35	3.49	3.10	2.87	2.71	2.60	2.51	2.45	2.39	2.35	2.28	2.20	2.12	2.04	1.95	1.90	1.84
21	4.32	3.47	3.07	2.84	2.68	2.57	2.49	2.42	2.37	2.32	2.25	2.18	2.10	2.01	1.92	1.87	1.81
22	4.30	3.44	3.05	2.82	2.66	2.55	2.46	2.40	2.34	2.30	2.23	2.15	2.07	1.98	1.89	1.84	1.78
23	4.28	3.42	3.03	2.80	2.64	2.53	2.44	2.37	2.32	2.27	2.20	2.13	2.05	1.96	1.86	1.81	1.76
24	4.26	3.40	3.01	2.78	2.62	2.51	2.42	2.36	2.30	2.25	2.18	2.11	2.03	1.94	1.84	1.79	1.73
25	4.24	3.39	2.99	2.76	2.60	2.49	2.40	2.34	2.28	2.24	2.16	2.09	2.01	1.92	1.82	1.77	1.71
26	4.23	3.37	2.98	2.74	2.59	2.47	2.39	2.32	2.27	2.22	2.15	2.07	1.99	1.90	1.80	1.75	1.69
27	4.21	3.35	2.96	2.73	2.57	2.46	2.37	2.31	2.25	2.20	2.13	2.06	1.97	1.88	1.79	1.73	1.67
28	4.20	3.34	2.95	2.71	2.56	2.45	2.36	2.29	2.24	2.19	2.12	2.04	1.96	1.87	1.77	1.71	1.65
29	4.18	3.33	2.93	2.70	2.55	2.43	2.35	2.28	2.22	2.18	2.10	2.03	1.94	1.85	1.75	1.70	1.64
30	4.17	3.32	2.92	2.69	2.53	2.42	2.33	2.27	2.21	2.16	2.09	2.01	1.93	1.84	1.74	1.68	1.62
40	4.08	3.23	2.84	2.61	2.45	2.34	2.25	2.18	2.12	2.08	2.00	1.92	1.84	1.74	1.64	1.58	1.51
60	4.00	3.15	2.76	2.53	2.37	2.25	2.17	2.10	2.04	1.99	1.92	1.84	1.75	1.65	1.53	1.47	1.39
120	3.92	3.07	2.68	2.45	2.29	2.17	2.09	2.02	1.96	1.91	1.83	1.75	1.66	1.55	1.43	1.35	1.25
∞	3.84	3.00	2.60	2.37	2.21	2.10	2.01	1.94	1.88	1.83	1.75	1.67	1.57	1.46	1.32	1.22	1.00

← Degrees of Freedom of the Denominator

Table E

Values of F for 99% Level of Certainty

Degrees of Freedom of the Numerator

Den. df	1	2	3	4	5	6	7	8	9	10	12	15	20	30	60	120	∞
1	4052	4999.5	5403	5625	5764	5859	5928	5982	6022	6056	6106	6157	6209	6261	6313	6339	6366
2	98.50	99.00	99.17	99.25	99.30	99.33	99.36	99.37	99.39	99.40	99.42	99.43	99.45	99.47	99.48	99.49	99.50
3	34.12	30.82	29.46	28.71	28.24	27.91	27.67	27.49	27.35	27.23	27.05	26.87	26.69	26.50	26.32	26.22	26.13
4	21.20	18.00	16.69	15.98	15.52	15.21	14.98	14.80	14.66	14.55	14.37	14.20	14.02	13.84	13.65	13.56	13.46
5	16.26	13.27	12.06	11.39	10.97	10.67	10.46	10.29	10.16	10.05	9.89	9.72	9.55	9.38	9.20	9.11	9.02
6	13.75	10.92	9.78	9.15	8.75	8.47	8.26	8.10	7.98	7.87	7.72	7.56	7.40	7.23	7.06	6.97	6.88
7	12.25	9.55	8.45	7.85	7.46	7.19	6.99	6.84	6.72	6.62	6.47	6.31	6.16	5.99	5.82	5.74	5.65
8	11.26	8.65	7.59	7.01	6.63	6.37	6.18	6.03	5.91	5.81	5.67	5.52	5.36	5.20	5.03	4.95	4.86
9	10.56	8.02	6.99	6.42	6.06	5.80	5.61	5.47	5.35	5.26	5.11	4.96	4.81	4.65	4.48	4.40	4.31
10	10.04	7.56	6.55	5.99	5.64	5.39	5.20	5.06	4.94	4.85	4.71	4.56	4.41	4.25	4.08	4.00	3.91
11	9.65	7.21	6.22	5.67	5.32	5.07	4.89	4.74	4.63	4.54	4.40	4.25	4.10	3.94	3.78	3.69	3.60
12	9.33	6.93	5.95	5.41	5.06	4.82	4.64	4.50	4.39	4.30	4.16	4.01	3.86	3.70	3.54	3.45	3.36
13	9.07	6.70	5.74	5.21	4.86	4.62	4.44	4.30	4.19	4.10	3.96	3.82	3.66	3.51	3.34	3.25	3.17
14	8.86	6.51	5.56	5.04	4.69	4.46	4.28	4.14	4.03	3.94	3.80	3.66	3.51	3.35	3.18	3.09	3.00
15	8.68	6.36	5.42	4.89	4.56	4.32	4.14	4.00	3.89	3.80	3.67	3.52	3.37	3.21	3.05	2.96	2.87
16	8.53	6.23	5.29	4.77	4.44	4.20	4.03	3.89	3.78	3.69	3.55	3.41	3.26	3.10	2.93	2.84	2.75
17	8.40	6.11	5.18	4.67	4.34	4.10	3.93	3.79	3.68	3.59	3.46	3.31	3.16	3.00	2.83	2.75	2.65
18	8.29	6.01	5.09	4.58	4.25	4.01	3.84	3.71	3.60	3.51	3.37	3.23	3.08	2.92	2.75	2.66	2.57
19	8.18	5.93	5.01	4.50	4.17	3.94	3.77	3.63	3.52	3.43	3.30	3.15	3.00	2.84	2.67	2.58	2.49
20	8.10	5.85	4.94	4.43	4.10	3.87	3.70	3.56	3.46	3.37	3.23	3.09	2.94	2.78	2.61	2.52	2.42
21	8.02	5.78	4.87	4.37	4.04	3.81	3.64	3.51	3.40	3.31	3.17	3.03	2.88	2.72	2.55	2.46	2.36
22	7.95	5.72	4.82	4.31	3.99	3.76	3.59	3.45	3.35	3.26	3.12	2.98	2.83	2.67	2.50	2.40	2.31
23	7.88	5.66	4.76	4.26	3.94	3.71	3.54	3.41	3.30	3.21	3.07	2.93	2.78	2.62	2.45	2.35	2.26
24	7.82	5.61	4.72	4.22	3.90	3.67	3.50	3.36	3.26	3.17	3.03	2.89	2.74	2.58	2.40	2.31	2.21
25	7.77	5.57	4.68	4.18	3.85	3.63	3.46	3.32	3.22	3.13	2.99	2.85	2.70	2.54	2.36	2.27	2.17
26	7.72	5.53	4.64	4.14	3.82	3.59	3.42	3.29	3.18	3.09	2.96	2.81	2.66	2.50	2.33	2.23	2.13
27	7.68	5.49	4.60	4.11	3.78	3.56	3.39	3.26	3.15	3.06	2.93	2.78	2.63	2.47	2.29	2.20	2.10
28	7.64	5.45	4.57	4.07	3.75	3.53	3.36	3.23	3.12	3.03	2.90	2.75	2.60	2.44	2.26	2.17	2.06
29	7.60	5.42	4.54	4.04	3.73	3.50	3.33	3.20	3.09	3.00	2.87	2.73	2.57	2.41	2.23	2.14	2.03
30	7.56	5.39	4.51	4.02	3.70	3.47	3.30	3.17	3.07	2.98	2.84	2.70	2.55	2.39	2.21	2.11	2.01
40	7.31	5.18	4.31	3.83	3.51	3.29	3.12	2.99	2.89	2.80	2.66	2.52	2.37	2.20	2.02	1.92	1.80
60	7.08	4.98	4.13	3.65	3.34	3.12	2.95	2.82	2.72	2.63	2.50	2.35	2.20	2.03	1.84	1.73	1.60
120	6.85	4.79	3.95	3.48	3.17	2.96	2.79	2.66	2.56	2.47	2.34	2.19	2.03	1.86	1.66	1.53	1.38
∞	6.63	4.61	3.78	3.32	3.02	2.80	2.64	2.51	2.41	2.32	2.18	2.04	1.88	1.70	1.47	1.32	1.00

Degrees of Freedom of the Denominator

Bibliography

Anthony, Robert N. and Glen A. Welsch. *Fundamentals of Management Accounting.* Homewood, Illinois: Richard D. Irwin, 1974.

Anthony, Robert N. and James S. Reece. *Management Accounting Text and Cases.* Fifth edition. Homewood, Illinois: Richard D. Irwin, 1975.

Chou, Ya-lun. *Statistical Analysis.* New York: Holt, Rinehart and Winston, 1975.

Ferguson, George A. *Statistical Analysis in Psychology and Education.* New York: McGraw-Hill Book Company, 1966.

Freund, John E. *Mathematical Statistics.* Englewood Cliffs, New Jersey: Prentice-Hall, Inc., 1962.

Horngren, Charles T. *Accounting for Management Control.* Englewood Cliffs, New Jersey: Prentice-Hall, Inc., 1974.

Horngren, Charles T. *Cost Accounting: A Managerial Emphasis.* Englewood Cliffs, New Jersey: Prentice-Hall, Inc., 1972.

Hummel, Paul M. and Charles Seebeck. *Mathematics of Finance.* New York: McGraw-Hill Book Company, 1971.

Weston, J. Fred and Eugene F. Brigham. *Essentials of Managerial Finance.* Third edition. Hinsdale, Illinois: The Dryden Press, 1974.

Index